make the crossing by a ford or ferry. The nearest ford to Barton was a short distance downstream from the present bridges, and it was the only means of crossing the river until the mid-seventeenth century.

Wise men wishing to cross water look first at the geology of the site and the geography of the area. The present bridges and their predecessors were built on beds of sandstone through which the river has worn a steep-sided valley. Fords, on the other hand, required relatively shallow water and moderate currents, like those met with further downstream where the river reaches softer gravels which have allowed a wider channel to evolve. Chat Moss was largely impassable and the township of Barton was probably the nearest place to Manchester where fording the Irwell was possible; thus it became a recognised crossing.

Late nineteenth century industrialisation of the Barton area hides the original, bleak, open landscape with a wide river meandering between the Cheshire plain and the rising ground of Lancashire - a river of treacherous bed in summer and winter floods, each mood designed to trap the unwary traveller. In 1628, inhabitants of local parishes testified that the ferry boat was in such a bad state that horses could hardly be carried and that floods deposited quicksands; even when the water level had dropped, 'people passe with great danger of drowneing & often over throwne in the water.'

The problems of building a bridge in a river as large and unpredictable as the Irwell were considerable, although well understood by the practical masons of the time. It was crucial to provide supporting pillars in the stream bed, since only relatively short spans are possible in masonry.

There were two basic ways of building bridge piers. The more effective, not used at Barton until the 1890s, diverted the river through a temporary channel so that the whole operation could be undertaken 'in the dry'. When construction of the bridge was completed, the waters were returned to their original course.

Possibly less expensive, but technically more demanding and posing greater risk to workers' lives, was the method used at Barton in the seventeenth and eighteenth centuries. This involved excluding the waters from an isolated section of the river bed by erecting a coffer dam, or caisson, round the selected site, a procedure usually undertaken in summer drought conditions. It involved driving piles side by side into the river bed, forming a barrier to withstand shallow water. Two concentric palisades were needed to keep the water out completely, especially where it was deeper or swift-moving. The space between was filled with clay, well stamped down, to form a continuous, virtually waterproof wall. This is the

prec
'pu
eng........
removed from the centre by pumps and buckets, work could continue on the river bed.

If the river bed was not firm enough to take the weight of the pier, timber piles had to be driven into it until a sufficiently firm area was created. Masonry work could then proceed and the piers would be raised to the height needed to begin building the arches.

During the construction of the arch a complex and strong timber framework, called 'centering' or 'false work' and extending to the full width and span of the intended arch, was required to support the weight of the masonry. The arches would be built either of wedge-shaped stones known as voussoirs or of several courses of brick, which once the arch is completed are self-supporting. When the final, or 'key' stone, was fixed, the temporary timber centering was removed. Building up the side walls, called spandrels, then providing a road surface, completed the bridge.

An example of timber centering for bridge arches. The photograph was taken when the Ship Canal was being built, possibly at Irlam

The Masonry Road Bridge

Elizabethan accounts of travel near the Barton river crossing suggest that it was a journey undertaken by very basic means. For the most part ordinary folk travelled on foot, overtaken by the gentry riding on horseback to visits or on business. The heavier commerce was restricted to pack horses and the roads themselves were little more than trackways, not paved in any real sense. Wheeled traffic was virtually unknown, and certainly few would attempt using the ford, which at this time was the natural river bed of mud, gravel and sand, forever shifting and constantly varying in width and depth.

As the volume of traffic using the crossing at Barton increased, there was presumably an increase in casualties losing their dignity - or, worse, their lives. The

problem eventually became such that in 1628 the inhabitants of the parishes of Eccles, Flixton and Stretford petitioned the Justices in the Hundred of Salford for a bridge to be built at Barton. The Court of Quarter Session considered the petition, and ordered that a sum of £140 be collected within the Hundred of Salford 'for the erecting & building of a stone bridge in Barton' over the River Irwell. If this bridge were ever built at all, it must have quickly become inadequate or derelict, because in 1672 the Justices of the County Palatine of Chester themselves petitioned the Lancashire Justices that a bridge be built at the Barton crossing.

The unusual step of cross-county negotiations is borne out by the details in the petition. The importance of the route to trade between the two counties is emphasised, as is the perilous

nature of the crossing, for 'not onely many persons by reason of the frequent & great overflowinge of the waters there have been stopped in bringinge and carryinge of Coales and other carriages out of Lancashire into Cheshire & elsewhere, but also divers persons have lately lost their lives in indeavoringe to passe over the same.'

This petition apparently met with success, for in January 1676 the first payments were made - to men engaged in preliminary works which must have begun the previous year. The site chosen for the bridge was some distance upstream from the ford, and this was probably less because of the need to keep the ford open than because the underlying rock upstream was more suitable for the founding of pillars.

Most of the stone used in its construction came from quarries at Worsley; a total of nearly 5,000 loads was transported by local cart owners, most likely farmers

Transporting goods in Elizabethan times - a pack horse train

putting surplus capacity to profit. For the two-and-a-half mile journey along the unmade road the going rate was 1s6d a load in winter and 1s3d in summer. A further 36 loads of stone were carried the seven miles from Ringley. Other items in the accounts include 950 loads of Derbyshire lime, carried at 2s the load; this was mixed with local sand brought to the site to make the mortar.

While the records detail the materials purchased, they only suggest the construction methods used. Undoubtedly there would have been a coffer dam of sorts; alder wood 'pyles' were bought, but whether for a single or double skin coffer dam is uncertain. However, money was paid for 'gripyarding', and one meaning of this word is the making of hurdles of stakes and interwoven laths to retain earth; such barriers were often used to control watercourses.

The workers driving the piles into the riverbed and those later employed in removing the water undertook a dangerous and extremely uncomfortable job. In all likelihood permanently wet through, they

A chain pump being operated by a water wheel; from an old drawing

used the most primitive of equipment. Had they known it, they would perhaps have been thankful that the water was still almost drinkable, not the open sewer it was to become.

The accounts show payments for labour and equipment to keep the coffer dams dry whilst

the pillars were built and the mortar set. Pumps and chains, leather for the chains, buckets and scoops were purchased. The word 'pumps' could mean either force pumps or chain pumps, both of which were used. Chain pumps had been a feature of mining and civil engineering operations since

Paid for Turninge the water whilste the Pillers weare setting ffor Pumps Bucketts and there Appurtenances	
Imprimis for carriinge Pumps and Cheaynes from Dunham and ffrom Major Buckleys	00-04-00
It[em] one Pumpe and Cheayne ffrom middle Hulton	00-02-06
It[em] to John Romsbottome and his two brothers ffor boardinge and makeinge Pumps and there severall days attendance	02-03-04
It[em] to Robert Heaworth ffor Chaynes and hoockes	01-00-00
It[em] to Gyles Higson ffor Chaynes and leather	00-07-06

Items from the Barton Bridge Account Book, 1675/6. These relate to the supply and use of pumps and chains to keep the coffer dams dry (LRO: QSP/535/12)

the middle ages, and consisted of wads of leather attached to an endless chain which drew the water up a pipe barrel. They were better adapted to the removal of gritty or muddy water than the force pumps, which worked by pistons within a cylinder passing the water through valves which could become clogged or wear out. Resort was often made to using the scoops to 'lave' or bail out water, frequently on an overnight basis for which premium payments would be made, most likely in beer.

A lot of sturdy and precise carpentry work would be needed to provide the centering for the arches, and the accounts reflect payments for this and for wood, sometimes specified as oak, ash, birch or poplar. Women were employed in the most menial and unpleasant tasks, mainly to carry baskets of

Carpenters and their tools; a drawing based on an early woodcut

sand (for the mortar) from out of the water, and a man was paid 9d per day to help fill the baskets and lift them on to the women's heads. Expenses were also paid for rent for land to store materials, and for use as a mason's workyard in the

It[em] paid ffor nyne hundred and ffiftie loades of lyme brought out of Darbishire att two shillings the loade is — 95-00-00

Imprimis carriinge and leadinge sand and earth and ffilling sand and earth & other worke about the Bridge as ffollow

It[em] to severall women for Carringe sand in wisketts out of the water to make morter on 113 days worke at 5d per diem is — 02-07-01

It[em] to Hugh Pollet for 20 days worke to helpe the women to ffill there wiskets and to helpt them to there heads at 9d per diem — 00-15-00

It[em] to Henerie Knight John Be[i?]rch & Hugh Pollet everie of them six days at 9d per diem to ffill sand and earth — 00-13-06

It[em] paid Rich: Crosbie William Jackson John Scoales and William Parren 60 days at 9d per diem to fill carts with earth & sand — 02-05-00

Entries from the Barton Bridge Account Book, showing a large payment for Derbyshire limestone and small payments to the women who carried baskets of wet sand on their heads (LRO: QSP/535/12)

preparation of the stone brought by cart.

Here the freshly hewn stone, roughly squared at the Worsley quarries, would be trimmed to the exact size and profile by the 'banker masons' before passing to the hands of the 'fixer masons' for placing into position. Not mentioned in the accounts, but doubtless used, would be simple hand- or animal-powered cranes to manoeuvre the blocks. It is likely that the work site was also used for the burning and slaking of the Derbyshire limestone, before it could be combined with the sand for mortar. This is an effective mixture, waterproof and tenacious. Its only drawback is the lengthy drying time needed, a factor which was to be of some significance.

Construction and contractual difficulties beset the project. At Easter 1677, the four masonry contractors, Mathew Travis, John Sandiforth, Christopher Hindle and John Hindle, petitioned the Justices at Manchester, stating how they undertook to do the work and to 'uphold itt for one whole yeare after itt should bee perfectly finished'. But there was a violent rainstorm before the mortar in the centre pillar had set and the flood 'overturned the whole'.

When the bridge collapsed, the masons were sued for breach of contract and forced to rebuild at their own expense, a task which later petitions show they did not finish until 1684. The masons further stated that the original articles had been for a bridge with two pillars and three arches, but the overseers of the rebuild considered that the original planned length would be too short and ordered another pillar and one more arch to be made. It was agreed that £100 should be paid for the extra arch and pillar and £24 for repairing the overturned portion.

The total cost of the bridge came to just over £1,121, which was £21 more than the £1,100 allowed for the work. The payment to the masons was £400, of which they had only received £350 in 1679 and final settlement of their accounts took until 1687. The whole project appears to have been beset by litigation between the various parties - the masons, surveyors and Justices of the counties and districts involved - and it is possible this friction caused inferior work to be produced.

As early as 1680, local residents petitioned that notwithstanding the money having been collected, Barton Bridge was still without battlements and unpaved, so that 'passengers & cattell bee in danger to bee thronne of [thrown off]'; the south arch was also unsafe due to the washing away of sand and gravel from its foot, suggesting the river bed had not been piled. Further heavy repairs became necessary in 1701.

Paid ffor Repaireinge the boate the mans paines helpinge the masson over the water and ffor A house to lay lyme in winter as ffolloweth

Imprimis to the boateman towards the Repaire of his Boate	05-00-00
It[em] ffor Helpinge the masson over the water	01-00-00
It[em] ffor A House to laye lyme in winter	00-10-00
It[em] ffor makinge A platte to Carrie stone over and a Coate ffor the masson to worke in winter	00-10-00
[...] ffor land to laye all other matereall upon to Mr Tho: Sorocold	
[Senr?] Thomas Newton and Raphe Turner	04-10-00
	11-10-00

From the Barton Bridge Accounts. The entries reflect some of difficulties faced by those working on the bridge, especially in winter (LRO: QSP/535/12)

When the Mersey & Irwell Navigation was formed, the river bank was improved and at some time between 1720 and 1735 a towpath was added beneath the arch on the Eccles side of the river. Whilst extensive works were undertaken in the Barton area in this transformation of the river, only the addition of a timber pedestrian walkway bracketed out from the pier disfigured the bridge.

In the mid-eighteenth century the population of south Lancashire may well have been in a state of panic. Certainly the authorities were in some consternation, as the area was likely to become a battleground. During November of 1745 the rebels supporting the Young Pretender, better known as 'Bonnie Prince Charlie', were advancing southwards. The English authorities were uncertain as to whether they were bound for London or North Wales. So fast was the advance that the English forces could not be moved to confront them before the rebels reached south Lancashire and after some hesitation, it was decided to break down bridges on the Lancashire-Cheshire border to impede the rebels' advance.

The bridge at Barton was virtually demolished when the two central arches were broken down by soldiers of the Liverpool Blues regiment. In the event, the Jacobite rebels took the route through Manchester and then towards Derby.

The disruption of this important route was a severe handicap to local business and after the troubles were over, repair of the bridge was quickly ordered. By this date commercial operations had expanded way beyond the level of trade which had created the need for a bridge some seventy years earlier. It was only another fifteen years before the Bridgewater Canal was built to

---

SCOTCH AFFAIRS.

Copy of a Letter to a Gentleman in Manchester, dated New-castle, November 19.

It now seems too true, that the City and Castle of Carlisle are taken by the Rebels, who 'tis said have entrenched themselves to the Chin under the Walls, determin'd to wait for our Army there.

The Loss of Carlisle is deeply regretted, not only on Account of the innocent Inhabitants, who certainly suffer very egregiously, but the vast Quantity of Effects and Money belonging to Gentlemen in the Neighbourhood, and the Cannon and Ammunition's having fallen into the Hands of the Rebels, who will have a vast Advantage of our Army in employing the Cannon, &c. against us.

A Copy of a Letter from Penrith, dated Nov. 20, at 12 o' Clock at Night,

The Highlanders have been coming in here ever since four o'clock this Afternoon till Nine. Some Houses have 100 a piece in. The whole Body we have good Reason to believe are moving Southward. We have 3000 in Town, what is in the Neighbourhood we cannot yet Judge. To-morrow is to bring us several Thousands more.

From an edition of the Manchester Gazette, 1745. Reports of the Jacobite menace moving south led to the decision to pull down Barton Bridge

---

meet the demand. In January 1746, the Lancashire Court of Quarter Sessions ordered the construction of wooden bridges at Barton and Crossford as temporary replacements for the bridges destroyed in the emergency.

Permanent reconstruction was not long delayed, for in 1749 the Surveyor of Barton Bridge gave information to the court about the condition of the structure. It is evident that some rebuilding had taken place, for although his report describes 50 yards of battlements as being out of repair, 'several yards thereof being fallen off', the 'new or late erected' arch and battlement was not out of repair. Another witness was examined, 'touching that part of Barton Bridge which was lately pulld down and rebuilt by John Gatliffe.'

The new bridge was built as a three-arch structure. The central arch had a span of 55 feet and the north and south arches spanned 30 feet. There was an additional small arch, intended to carry flood water, situated 'at the distance of 130 feet', but the records don't say on which bank this was located. The roadway, described by the Surveyor as early as 1782 as being 'much too narrow', was only thirteen feet wide. Barton Bridge was then listed as one of the two county bridges within the Hundred of Salford.

Whilst little is known of the appearance of the bridge completed at the second attempt by the disgruntled seventeenth-century masons, engravings and photographs exist which show the post-Jacobite repair. The roadway had an appreciable rise to the centre arch but it could not be called a hump-backed bridge. The original approach may have been by short, very steep ramps, particularly on the Eccles bank; this was later replaced by a longer embankment.

In early nineteenth century views the downstream - west - face is presumed to be the original, or at least that rebuilt by John Gatliffe. He had provided two courses of arch voussoirs; the first to be laid was the inner one, recessed from the subsequent course and side walls. The spandrel walls - or sides - were of evenly coursed ashlar - the high quality masonry where the stones are of regular, fully squared form laid with thin joints. In this case the facing was either deliberately rusticated to begin with, or has been heavily weathered over time.

The stones were laid to match the rise of the roadway, where a protruding string course emphasised the road surface level. A parapet of identical faced stone completed the face. Massive cutwaters rose to flood level, beyond which only a decorative, protruding pillar continued to the string course level.

Ringley Bridge in the early nineteenth century. It hasn't changed much!

A good indication of the bridge's appearance from a road user's viewpoint can be got by a visit to Ringley Bridge, across the same River Irwell. Its narrowness, camber and length, particularly when viewed with the river in flood, must give a realistic impression of conditions at Barton before the modifications carried out later.

Comparable changes to the condition of the road took a

The downstream face of Barton Bridge, showing the two courses of arch voussoirs. A pillar of the stone aqueduct can be seen through the arch

further seventy-five years. In May 1825 an Act was finally gained to improve the road between Barton Bridge and what became Moses Gate near Bolton. Users of this new turnpike had to pay, although the bridge remained a free passage, and this was the situation until the charges were abolished in November 1871. There had been an earlier, but illegal, attempt to demand payment for use of the road to the south of the bridge in 1685 by Mr Trafford (of Trafford Park) or his agents. They argued that this was to compensate the tenants for land given up in making the new approach road to the bridge, a deviation from the route to the ford. On this basis Mr. Trafford 'did nothinke' to countermand the setting up of the toll gate.

To the great relief of road users, Lancashire County Council finally undertook the widening of Barton Bridge in 1830 with Charles Carrington, the County Bridge Surveyor, directing operations. The work was described as being sufficient 'for two carts to pass'. The extension was built on the upstream side and the keystone of the upstream arch suitably

inscribed as a commemoration tablet.

The design of the upstream face overseen by Mr Carrington in 1830 was much more technically demanding, and presumably more expensive than the downstream face. The point of this remains a mystery. Photographs show that a protruding string course at road level and parapet of coursed ashlar were, in fact, identical with the other face. Below the road level the whole spandrel area was formed of voussoir-like radial stones with a heavily rusticated face. This would appear to have been an attempt to imitate the style of the Barton Lane aqueduct that was carrying the Bridgewater Canal by the time these additions were made.

Substantial cutwaters were provided to the pillars, these continuing to taper upwards to the string course. Viewed from above, the parapet was straight on both sides. There was no buttress continued at parapet level, unlike the bridge at Ringley, where the continuation gives a triangular protrusion at the pillars to provide a pedestrian refuge point.

The inscribed keystone from the 1830 widening of the bridge

Old Barton Bridge was demolished to make way for the building of the swing bridge on the construction of the Manchester Ship Canal. The Eccles Journal of Friday 10th April 1891 details its closure: 'The traffic over Barton Bridge is to be stopped at 6 o'clock this (Friday) night, and the traffic will go over the canal by means of the temporary wooden bridge.' Demolition work began immediately.

The upstream face of the bridge as reconstructed in 1830

The Mersey & Irwell Navigation Company

The River Irwell was converted to a 'Navigation' in an attempt to relieve the transport problems existing between Manchester and Liverpool at the beginning of the eighteenth century. Traffic, particularly in goods, had grown and the potential for further increases would have been seen by the merchants and manufacturers of both towns. The roads were busier but the carts and surfaces available could not have dealt with the volume envisaged. It was common practice to use rivers as commercial highways, but the Mersey and Irwell system was not passable to cargo boats upstream of Warrington.

The most practical solution available at the time was to improve the existing waterway. A group of merchants with venture capital formed the Mersey & Irwell Navigation Company to undertake the task.

An Act for making the Rivers *Mercy* and *Irwell* Navigable from *Liverpoole* to *Mancheſter*, in the County-Palatine of *Lancaſter*.

Whereas the making and keeping the Rivers Mercy and Irwell in the Counties Palatine of Lancaster and Cheſter, Navigable and Paſſable for Boats, Barges, Lighters, and other Veſſels, from Liverpoole in the ſaid County of Lancaſter, up the ſaid Rivers Mercy and Irwell, to a Place called Hunts-bank in Mancheſter in the ſaid County of Lancaſter, will be very beneficial to Trade, advantageous to the Poor, and convenient for the Carriage of Coals, Cannel, Stone, Timber, and other Goods, Wares, and Merchandizes, to and from the Towns and Parts adjacent, and will very much tend to the Imploying and Increaſe of Watermen and Seamen, and be a Means to preſerve the Highways: May it therefore pleaſe Your moſt Excellent Majeſty, that it may be Enacted; and be it Enacted by the Kings moſt Excellent Majeſty, by and with the Advice and Conſent of the Lords Spiritual and Temporal, and Commons in this preſent Parliament aſſembled, and by the Authority of the ſame, That Oſwald Moſley of Ancotes, George Kenyon of Peele, Eſqs; Joſeph Yates, John Leech, Joſeph Byrom, Ralph Houghton, James Bradſhaw, Joſeph Vigor, John Lees, Samuel Clowes, James Bayley, Mathew Greaves, Jeremiah Bowers, William Shrigley, William Holme, Francis Davenport, James Marſden,

Ppp 2   Richard

The first page of the Mersey and Irwell Act of 1720

Barton Lock, on the north side of the Irwell, upstream of the aqueduct and road bridge. All Saints School can be seen in the background

Powers to proceed with the work were obtained in an Act of Parliament in 1720. The company was granted the right to manage navigation on the rivers Mersey and Irwell from Liverpool to Hunts Bank in Manchester. Thomas Steers - a pioneer navigation, dock and canal civil engineer - was appointed and, at first under his direction, work proceeded intermittently, until by 1737 boats of 50 tons burden were able to reach the Old Quay, Manchester.

The entrepreneurs had arranged to control the river flow and water depth by reinforcing and realigning the banks and to maintain the vital summer water level by a series of weirs. Pound locks - the type used on canals - were included in the weir structure so that boats could pass. In return for its outlay, the company was entitled to levy tolls on users.

The improvements were very evident at Barton, for just upstream of the road bridge they built a weir and lock. The lock was situated on the north, or Eccles bank, with the river

water passing over a weir on the Stretford side. A quay was provided to cater for trade from the length of highway served by the bridge and for any local business from Eccles.

There are several references to sail boats, particularly by the Baron Dupin, a member of the academic Institute of France who visited in 1825 and described how 'vessels on the Irwell pass in full sail through the middle arch.' But in the early days the main source of propulsion, particularly upstream, was bow hauling. Teams of men - rarely horses - plodded along the ill-defined towpath, pulling on a rope secured high on the boat mast so as to clear waterside obstructions.

The main line of towpath west of Barton was on the south side of the river navigation, so boats had to be hauled through the arch of Barton bridge on the walkway that had been provided under the arch on the Eccles side, whilst the 'halers', as the men were known, crossed the waterway by the bridge almost in the manner of a roving bridge as used on later

canals. From Barton, they were able to continue towards Manchester along the towpath on the north bank.

This waterway provided the needed stimulus to trade and soon gained a competitor in the form of the Bridgewater Canal. In later years, faced with the dual competition of the canal and the Liverpool to Manchester railway, the Navigation Company made substantial improvements. Extensive - and doubtless expensive - civil engineering operations were carried out in 1840 to widen and deepen the watercourse, so that sea-going vessels of up to 300 tons cargo capacity could reach Manchester.

Photographs of Barton in the 1880s show features which may have been part of these improvements. A cobbled roadway beginning at the bridge abutment on the north, or Eccles bank, gave direct access to the quay and lock. On the south, or Stretford bank, a ramp climbed from the river towpath level to join what is now Redclyffe Road a few yards away from the bridge.

A nineteenth century painting showing the ramp rising from the south bank of the river to join the road leading to Stretford

The Masonry Aqueduct

John Gilbert

Francis Egerton, Third Duke of Bridgewater, is credited with being the 'father of inland navigation' as the promoter of the pioneering Bridgewater Canal. In fact, two previous attempts to provide canal transport through Worsley to Manchester had been made, one in the lifetime of his father, the first Duke. Scroop Egerton had been a commissioner to arbitrate between the various parties when an Act to make the Worsley brook navigable to the Irwell at Barton was proposed, with the specific aim of transporting Worsley coal to Manchester. The promoters were a joint stock company backed by the Mersey & Irwell Navigation Company and the Act was obtained in 1737.

The second attempt was made in 1754, when Francis Egerton was only 18 years old and still a minor. It proposed a canal from Wigan, through Leigh and Worsley to Salford. Whilst promoted by Manchester business men, it was supported on the young Duke's behalf by his guardian, Samuel Egerton of Tatton Hall. Neither of these ventures was proceeded with.

When he came of age and took full control of his inheritance, Francis Egerton engaged John Gilbert, of Cotton in Staffordshire, as Agent to his Worsley estates. Gilbert brought his family to live in Worsley in June 1757 and immediately began a study of resources and deficits. His main responsibility was to keep the estates profitable, and he agreed with the Duke that capital should be expended on several projects, of which the canal to Manchester was the most important. A system of economic transport was clearly needed to improve the income from coal mining, and John Gilbert undertook the preliminary work of surveying a canal route and drafting details for the Bill submitted to Parliament on 25th November, 1758.

He attended the House on 6th December with the working plan, certifying that he had supervised the levelling and measuring of the ground for the proposed canal. Royal assent to

The familiar portrait of the Canal Duke against a background of Barton's bridges. Horses tow laden boats across the aqueduct, while men haul barges on the older navigation

the first Bridgewater Canal Act was obtained in March 1759, for a canal to follow the 82-foot contour from Worsley to Salford, remaining entirely on the north bank of the River Irwell. Its route is described in the Act as being from 'a croft or meadow, known by the name of Master Cooke's Tenter Croft, in the township of Salford... to or near Worsley Mill and Middlewood, in the said Manor of Worsley, and from thence to or near Hollin Ferry.' Work began immediately, as by the end of the year 1759 the section from Middlewood to Worsley, together with a two-mile advance towards Salford, had been dug to Monton.

But here there was to be a visibly abrupt change of course. It is evident that by late 1759 plans for the canal had been altered, probably with the intention of achieving a better route to Manchester and eventually, a strategic line to the Mersey. A period of frantic activity, involving a hurried, detailed survey and efforts to get Parliamentary approval for this major change to the first Act's authorised route, led to the building of the masonry aqueduct, now largely associated with James Brindley,

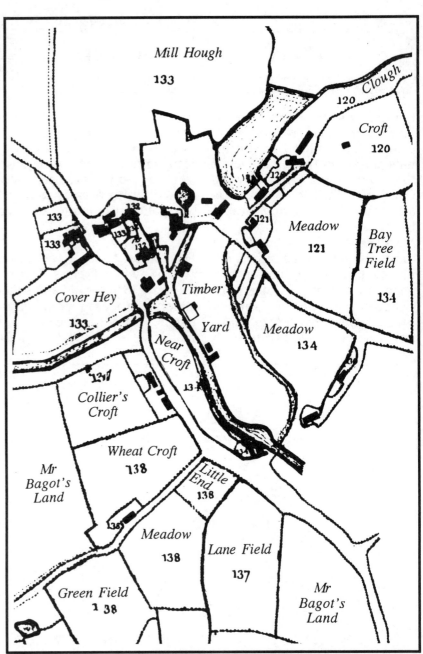

A copy of a 1764 plan of Worsley. Worsley Brow leads into the village from the left, Worsley Road goes off to the right and Barton Road is alongside the canal. The left hand branch of the canal leads towards Middlewood, named in the 1759 Act, and the northern arm to the Delph on the north side of Worsley Road, near Worsley Mill, which is also mentioned in the Act

James Brindley

to carry the Bridgewater Canal over the Irwell.

The first recorded presence of James Brindley at Worsley came in the July of 1759. Then still styling himself a 'millwright', Brindley brought his practical experience and skills to the project under the direction of John Gilbert. Who first thought of using an aqueduct is impossible to say, but there is now a greater realisation that the bulk of the preparatory

work was done by Gilbert. It is clear that he was heavily involved with the survey operations, collection of evidence and administration of the project in preparation for the submission to Parliament.

A Bill to make a canal 'from or near Worsley Mill, over the river Irwell, to the town of Manchester... and to or near Longford Bridge, in the township of Stretford' was submitted to Parliament on 13th

November 1759. In January of 1760, Brindley was in London to give evidence supporting this second Bridgewater Canal Bill, which abandoned the intended route into Salford and instead proposed crossing the Irwell by an aqueduct at Barton, then proceeding towards Stretford and Manchester. This would give access to a greater potential market than the earlier route.

Brindley, in his role of consulting engineer, undertook the task of convincing Parliament that the scheme was viable with all the flair of a modern television science programme presenter. It is said he demonstrated the principle of the aqueduct by carving a model from a cheese, and demonstrated the method of

waterproofing the arches by clay puddle by mixing the constituents, clay, sand and water, before the Committee of the House. In use, several layers of this material are trodden into the profile of the watercourse, providing an economic and reliable seal.

The modified canal would still follow the 82-foot contour, but with a three-arch masonry aqueduct to carry the waterway over the river at Barton - the subject of much ridicule by other engineers. The idea of boats passing over the River Irwell, on water 'within a watertight trunk of earth', was laughed at as the dream of a madman. At Brindley's own request, another engineer was brought in to report on the feasibility of the project. His

report to the Duke made the encouraging comment, 'I have often heard of castles in the air, but never before saw where one was to be erected.' Assent to an Act of Parliament for the aqueduct route was obtained in March 1760.

The Act is quite specific about the form the aqueduct had to take, largely to protect the viability of the existing Mersey & Irwell Navigation. Since the earlier Navigation was carried 'under and through three arches of the said bridge called Barton Bridge, and the boats and vessels are towed by men, who pass through one of the arches of the said bridge upon a towing-path made for that purpose,' the new canal had to have the same number of arches 'and lay the foundation of the piers upon which such new arches are to be raised in the bed of the said river.' So as not to impede the existing Navigation, 'such new arches shall not be made less in height and breadth than the present arches of the said bridge.' Just in case there was any misunderstanding, the arches were to be 'of such size and dimensions as shall be necessary and convenient for the purposes aforesaid.'

The Act also requires the Duke and his heirs to 'make, maintain, repair and support a good, substantial and convenient towing-path through such new arch of the said bridge', which was to link up with the towing-path under the arch of the existing [Barton] bridge. There was one contingency provision that was not proceeded with. The engineers could 'fix and adjoin the same [aqueduct] to the present piers and arches of the said [Barton] bridge, if he or they shall think fit.' Obviously they did not.

The site selected for the aqueduct was between the old bridge and the Navigation lock

A view through the arch on the Eccles side of the aqueduct, showing wooden railings along the edge of the towpath

and weir, about forty yards upstream of the bridge. Construction must have got under way immediately, as it is recorded that in July 1760 embankments were rising. In all, the works forming the aqueduct and its masonry approaches stretched some 600 feet. It was 36 feet wide at the top, the actual waterway being 18 feet wide and about 4½ feet deep. Each of the two side arches was 32 feet wide and the centre arch is variously described as having a span of between 57 and 62 feet. The towpath was on the western, or downstream side. The whole was to give a nominal 40-foot headroom over the river. Provision for stop gates was made at each end of the aqueduct, to isolate it from the canal should repairs be needed or for any emergency. Sluices allowed the water thus impounded to be discharged into the river, and spillways discharging into the river prevented overfilling of the aqueduct.

Whilst certainly most spectacular and rightly celebrated, the aqueduct formed only part of the works at Barton. On the north side of

June 10, 1760

This is to give Notice,

THAT the Commissioners appointed by Virtue of an Act of Parliament, entitled, An Act to enable the Most Noble Francis Duke of *Bridgewater*, to make a Navigable Cut or Canal, from a certain Place in the Township of *Salford*, to or near *Worsley Mill* and *Middlewood*, in the Manor of *Worsley*, and to or near a Place called *Hollin Ferry*, in the County Palatine of *Lancaster*, will, in Pursuance of an Adjournment of the said Commissioners, meet at the House of *John Dutton*, known by the Name of the *Old Coffee-House*, in *Manchester*, in the said County, on *Thursday* the 26th Day of *June* Inst. at three o'Clock in the Afternoon in order the more effectually to carry the Purposes of the said Act into Execution.

The summer of 1760 was a busy time for the Bridgewater Canal Commissioners. This notice for one of their monthly meetings appeared in the Manchester Mercury

the river it was approached by a long embankment which reached a height of twenty feet at the river bank. This hundred-yard-long embankment is now preserved and can be viewed from a walkway. It is formed with a stone face, finished in high quality ashlar, with stones sixteen inches thick and blocks up to six feet long. The wall is built to a 'batter', or inward slope to the top, of four horizontal to ten vertical units. A decorative moulding and coping surmounts the embankment and there are buttresses every twenty yards.

Another, but unremarked first was also contained in this long embankment - the first canal aqueduct across a public highway. Barton Lane runs parallel with the river about a hundred yards north of where the crossing was made and provision had to be made for the road traffic. To allow sufficient room for vehicles to pass beneath, the road had to be made into a cutting and a masonry arch carried the aqueduct over it. The arch matched the line of the embankment at 36 feet wide, but the bridge hole for the road was only 18 feet wide and some 12 feet to the crown of the arch. Masonry rose some ten feet above this point, thus allowing for the thickness of the arch, the waterproofing clay puddle and the depth of water.

For such a small structure its faces were of impressive proportions. The arch was flanked by wide pillars, whose stones had decorative bevelled joints, whilst the radial voussoirs of the arch were carried out to eight feet above the crown of the arch. A parapet tapered up from the level of the adjoining masonry

The impressive stonework of the bridge over Barton Lane, seen from the west side

embankment on both faces, and there was also a walkway on the eastern side (the opposite side to the canal towpath). Great use was made of the geology of the site, in that considerable portions of the structure were hewn from the natural rock. Surviving photographs reveal that the vertical sides supporting the arch over the roadway were of natural rock, as were portions of the spandrel pillars.

The construction methods for the aqueduct would have been much the same as for the road bridge. Piers would have been built using coffer dams founded within the river - an unpleasant task, as by then the water would have been contaminated with sewage and industrial waste flowing downstream from the expanding town of Manchester. Proficient carpenters - useful on any construction project to produce the cranes and access platforms needed - would have been required to make the timber centering upon which to spring the arches.

The stone used came from the Delph at Worsley, the starting point for the canal and the underground canal. This was one of the most extensively worked quarries of the district and the stone was transported by water for as far as possible; as the canal advanced towards the site, there was a reduced reliance on cart and horse teams. Some material could also have been delivered by the rival river navigation.

It is possible that the magnesium lime mortar used was an entirely local product, as by this time John Gilbert had established mining of the Sutton limestone which had been found on the Worsley estate near Middlewood. To process it, Gilbert had built a lime burning kiln at Worsley, adjacent to Barton Road and served by its own canal branch.

An eighteenth century painting of the Delph at Worsley, showing stone being loaded into canal boats

Contemporary reports, later descriptions and illustrations show the aqueduct to have been of sandstone set in lime mortar. In 1825 the Baron Dupin, one of many learned individuals attracted by the works, wrote that the stonework had been secured with iron cramps soldered into position. This is a method particularly suited to and universally used for the fixing of coping stones, to secure them against the mechanical damage to which they are prone. The good Baron saw only this, not the whole of the structural masonry. Both upstream supporting piers were provided with cutwaters, continuing up to coping stone level, the spandrels being of level-coursed ashlar work. It is evident from the many illustrations available that no parapet was ever supplied to either edge.

A description of the masonry work on the Barton section of the works would be incomplete without some mention of the great number of masons' marks visible in the surviving sections. Payment systems common at the time meant that within the overall terms of the contract each mason would be on piecework rates. Since this meant the mason was paid only for what was produced, he carved his personal mark on each stone laid. Simple, easy to chisel forms were used, and many variations are identifiable on the embankment wall between Barton Lane and the Irwell.

Crucial to the success of the aqueduct, and indeed the whole of the canal works, was the ability to remain watertight. For centuries the process and material known as 'puddling' has proved to be economic and effective. It is based on the fact that natural clay in an homogeneous mass resists water penetration. In use, the clay is spread on the intended watercourse bed or sides, in suitable layers. It is sprinkled with sand and watered, after which a gang of puddlers tramples the mass for as long as necessary to ensure all air is expelled and individual clods are fused. The number of layers used varies according to requirements. Provided the puddle is not allowed to dry out or be broken through by physical damage, it will retain its waterproof quality indefinitely.

Eventually Brindley, who had supervised the works in the capacity of Resident Engineer, was satisfied as to their integrity and it was time to let in the water. There was almost a disaster when part of the structure appeared to begin to buckle. At this point, Brindley gave up and made a hasty exit, to bed at his lodgings at the Bishop Blaize Inn at Stretford. John Gilbert had to step in to save the situation. Having closed off the aqueduct and drained the trough, he discovered that Brindley had been too liberal with the clay puddle at one side of the arch; as a result, the excess weight and outward pressure of the water had weakened the arch.

The puddle was removed and replaced by the correct quantity and the face, or spandrel, of the affected section was rebuilt. Happily, these measures proved effective.

Whatever problems had been overcome, the whole aqueduct enterprise was complete in a very short time. Baron Dupin's account claims a ten month period. This may be a fairly accurate figure for the building of the over-river section, as only eighteen months elapsed between the passing of the enabling Act and the opening.

This took place on Friday, 17th July 1761, and is described in the Manchester Mercury newspaper: 'His Grace the Duke of Bridgewater, with the Earl of Stamford... and several other Gentlemen, came to Barton to see the Water turned into the Canal over the River Irwell, which drew together a

great Number of Spectators; and it is with Pleasure we can inform the Publick, that the Experiment answered the most sanguine Expectations of every one who was present. As soon as the Water had risen to the Level of the Canal, a large Boat carrying upwards of 50 Tons, was towed along the New Part of the Canal over the Arches, across the River Irwell, which were so firm, secure, and compact, that not a single Drop of Water could be perceived to pass or ouze thro' any of them, although the Surface of the Water in the Canal is 38 Feet above the surface of the Navigable River under it. This Canal will be carried on to Manchester, with all Expedition; and we are credibly informed, will be completed before Lady-day next [1762], every seeming Difficulty being now removed, and that in the mean Time the subterraneous Navigation to the Colliery will

The puddling process changed little over the years. These men were photographed in 1893, working on a new section of the Bridgewater Canal leading up to the swing aqueduct

be perfected, so that we may expect to have such a supply of Coals, as will considerably reduce the Price to the Consumers, and that this Work will be of very great Use, as well as an Ornament, to the Town and Neighbourhood of Manchester.'

Justifiable cause for celebration, but proof of the load-carrying capacity of the finished aqueduct did not complete the venture. A through route to the wharves of the Manchester terminus at Castlefield was not achieved until 1764. Because of this delay there was a need to supply coal to Manchester by alternative means and it is known that great use was made of the Stretford to Manchester turnpike road, where coal transhipped to carts attracted a bulk traffic rate. There are also sufficient oblique references to suggest that coal and other goods were transhipped by hand crane over the side of the aqueduct, to and from boats on the river navigation below. Early illustrations of the aqueduct depict a crane mechanism on the Eccles arch section.

The word 'towed' in relation to the first boat to cross the

A detail from an eighteenth century view of the aqueduct, showing the framework of a hoist for transferring goods between boats on the Bridgewater Canal and on the river navigation

aqueduct is significant, for when the masonry aqueduct was being demolished in 1893, a discovery was made which suggested that the section forming the towpath was built after the rest of the structure.

The Farnworth Journal of 16th September reported that most of the hauling path had been cleared away down to the buttresses and, referring to an OLD facing revealed on the archway, continued, 'it would seem... that the path had been added at a later date to the aqueduct. That being so, it is evident that at one time boats passed over the aqueduct alone;

Barges heading towards Barton Lock on the old navigation. The cutwaters which were added to the aqueduct in the early nineteenth century are clearly visible

whilst the horses and mules had to deviate from their path and cross the Irwell by the old road.' If this theory is correct, the original plan would have been to punt boats over the aqueduct and take horses across Barton Lane and over Barton bridge to rejoin their charges on the other side of the river.

However, contemporary descriptions mention towing and several paintings, produced about 1770, show horses, complete with postillion, on the aqueduct. So if the towpath was not part of the original plan, it must have been added before the aqueduct was opened, perhaps at the time of Gilbert's repair.

There were certainly alterations to the aqueduct. Artists of the late eighteenth century were usually competent in their architectural views, so it is reasonable to accept their depictions of the structure. Paintings or engravings of the aqueduct produced before 1800 show features recognisably alike, with the only differences attributable to artistic licence or skill. Rousseau in 1769 and two other views published in 1770 and 1794 depict the downstream face, and another artist, contemporary with Rousseau, the upstream face.

All show flat-faced piers with a string course at arch spring level. Above this point, Rousseau alone has a decorative string course emphasising the central arch, set between the arch and the coping course. Above this stone coping, each artist shows a varying thickness of unretained earth, seemingly forming the navigation channel. All these early views show a structure beneath the south arch which in various sources is said to have been used as a mess room and 'dance hall' by workmen. It should be noted that 'dance floor' was a construction industry term for any close boarded platform such as a scaffold!

Later engravings, one published in 1864 and another about 1890, show a far different arrangement, with each face transformed. Photographs taken just prior to demolition bear out the accuracy of these later artists. The outer faces are shown to have piers with pointed cutwaters which continue beyond the spring of the arch, right up to a continuous horizontal coping course a short distance above the arch. All the masonry is of coursed ashlar, above which is a thick layer of unretained earth rising from the level of the waterway to provide pathways. The outermost portion of the piers is visibly wider than the remainder, and the arches are clearly shown to be composed of several rings of brickwork, with masonry only for decorative keystones.

Photographic views taken from the towpath, along the length of the aqueduct or across it, show the working arrangements. On the east or upstream side, and allowing for the thickness of masonry forming the outer face, an appreciable width of earth or cinder-topped walkway is discernible. The water channel is topped with a sandstone coping, presumably to minimise damage to the puddle

Looking along the aqueduct from the Eccles side, showing on the right the parapet of the bridge over Barton Lane, and the towpath complete with strollers, coping stones and wooden fence. On the left, the new swing aqueduct is under construction

from the wash of passing boats. The downstream or towpath side also had the stone kerb to the waterway and the greater portion of the towpath was flagstone paved, to prevent erosion from hooves. As already noted, neither side had any parapet, only a timber post and rail fence on the towpath edge.

Since the piers with cutwaters only appear on drawings published in Victorian times, the alterations were probably made in the early nineteenth century. A likely date for the work to have been carried out is indicated on the remaining portion of the original approach embankment. Two of the buttresses carry date plaques cut so as to stand proud of the stone. The buttress nearest Barton Lane has, within an elliptical shape, the legend 'WRB 1824'. Another, nearer the Ship Canal, appears only to have the date 1822.

The initials correspond with the name William Rigby Bradshaw, son of the Superintendent Trustee, Robert Haldane Bradshaw, and William is known to have been assisting his father in the early 1820s. There must have been a very compelling reason for the expenditure on the re-facing of the aqueduct and approach, as in those years the Bridgewater Trust was in its period of tightest financial stringency.

The statement made on the aqueduct's opening that the work was 'firm' and 'secure' was certainly proved true at the time of demolition. Farnworth Journal readers were informed that onlookers watching from the road bridge were much impressed by the substantial manner in which Barton Aqueduct had been built by Brindley and by the amount of labour needed to demolish it. 'Stone, brickwork, and mortar present such a solid front to the pick that very little impression

seems to be made by that instrument.' Even iron or steel wedges driven in by sledge hammers were resisted and 'So good is the lime [mortar] used for the stone facings that frequently the two stones have to be wedged asunder.' Eventually dynamite had to be used to expedite progress. The temporary embarrassment caused to Brindley and Gilbert by the partial collapse, in the days when canal building was an inexact science, was as nothing compared to future attempts at bridge building here at Barton.

Photographs of the aqueduct taken just before demolition reveal one purely operational feature which was the result of the form in which the aqueduct was constructed.

The Bridgewater Canal was built as a 'broad' canal to admit the boats then in common usage on the river navigations. These were the Mersey flats, a

style of trading boat of about 14 foot beam. The normal canal width allowed them to pass with ease. Surviving details of the aqueduct, however, show its waterway to be only 18 feet in width, and this meant one way traffic. With the intensity of working attained in the canal's heyday, this must have proved an operational nightmare and no doubt led to heated words and fisticuffs on occasion.

The solution is visible on several engravings and photographs. It would seem that a traffic signal was installed on the aqueduct to control access. Situated centrally on the arch at the Stretford bank, the pole is about 15 feet high with the signal being either of the disc and bar type or a true semaphore. One close-up photograph shows two arms on each side of the pole. The apparatus appears to be controlled by a ground frame of at least three levers.

The signalling mechanism on the Stretford side of the aqueduct is shown on this photograph taken in February 1891

The Bridgewater Navigation Company

In 1776, when the Bridgewater Canal was completed as a through route between Manchester and Liverpool, rivalry between the Duke's canal and the old river navigation became intense. Fortunately for both waterway promoters, there was an increase in regional trade in line with their hopes and predictions. In the year of the Duke's death, 1803, his canal carried about 6,500 tons per week, a total of some 334,500 tons in the year, about a third of which was coal.

In the early years of the succeeding Bridgewater Trust, created under the Duke's will to run his concerns, some accommodation was made with their rivals. In 1810 the two issued simultaneously identical tariffs of charges for goods carried. Soon afterwards, with the acceleration of growth in the Lancashire cotton industry following the Napoleonic wars, raw cotton and manufactured goods became the staple cargo for both. Such was the increase in this trade that by 1840, some 55,000 tons were carried on the Bridgewater Canal alone. Coal carried over the Barton aqueduct rarely failed to exceed

A list of Bridgewater Canal carriage charges published in 1810

100,000 tons per annum and by the mid-nineteenth century was closer to 200,000 tons yearly.

Both these carrying concerns faced the inherent disadvantages of being totally reliant on natural resources. Cargoes could be delayed, sometimes for weeks, by frost, drought or silting of the Mersey estuary upon which they both

depended. The Duke was far-sighted enough to recognise a potential competitor when he remarked to his Worsley neighbour, Lord Kenyon, that 'we shall do well enough if we can steer clear of those demmed tramroads.' His fears came to be a reality for his successors, as by the 1820s the merchants and manufacturers of Manchester and Liverpool, fed up with the poor service and high costs of the two waterways, were considering rail transport.

These gentlemen formed the Liverpool and Manchester Railway Company, and first applied for an Act of Parliament in 1825. This was rejected, following considerable opposition from the Bridgewater Trustees. By the time of the second attempt in 1826, the Trustees' beneficiary, Lord Stafford, had taken a 20% shareholding in the rail venture and the Bill passed Parliament with little opposition. Shortly

1843: the Old Quay Company reduces its rates in response to competition from the railways

after the excitement of the Rainhill trials, the line opened, with fatal ceremony, on 15th September 1830.

Within a short period of the railway opening, it was found that there was sufficient trade for all three carriers. Over the next fifteen years a series of alliances and hostilities occurred, involving various combinations of the three parties. The one most likely to break any agreement on rates was the Old Quay Company and to avoid further hostilities the Bridgewater Trustees decided to acquire the older navigation. Formalities were completed and the change of ownership allowed on 1st January, 1844. Whilst attempting to run the two waterways effectively, it became apparent that the artificial cut was the superior route and by the 1860s the river was used only for relatively local transport rather than as a through route.

Eventually, the struggle to maintain the two waterways and the likelihood of increased railway competition brought the Bridgewater Trustees actively to pursue sale of their navigation interests. Abortive attempts had been made to sell to railway companies, particularly the North Staffordshire Railway. Success came on 1st September 1872, with a completion of sale to William Price, chairman of the Midland Railway Company and Sir Edward Watkin, chairman of the Manchester, Sheffield and Lincolnshire Railway, for £1,115,000. These gentlemen then formed a joint stock company, the Bridgewater Navigation Company. The local newspapers carried the news to Worsley and Barton in printing joint statements, saying that a circular had been received from the Bridgewater Navigation Company, announcing, 'We have this day taken possession of the property [the canals] and

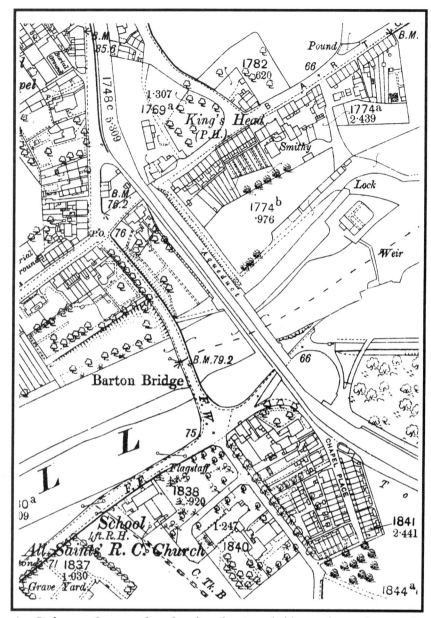

An Ordnance Survey plan showing the stone bridge and aqueduct on the eve of the changes brought by the Ship Canal Act. The lock and weir on the old navigation are still in place, but the old All Saints School, which stood between bridge and aqueduct, is no longer marked

hope to have your support to carry on the business.' It was signed by the Chairman, E W Watkin. There is an accompanying circular from Mr Fereday Smith, the general manager of the Bridgewater Trustees, confirming the transfer of the canals between Worsley, Manchester and Runcorn, and of the Mersey & Irwell Navigation.

It is evident that under its last two owners, the old river navigation was neglected. In 1840, shortly before purchase by the Bridgewater Trust, the

river was deepened and improved so that boats of 300 tons burden could navigate to Manchester, whilst by the 1880s the course was so silted as only to permit 50 ton boats on a few days a year. The real threat of a Ship Canal brought action plans from the Bridgewater Navigation Company, under the supervision of their engineer, Edward Leader Williams.

As late as January 1885, when the Manchester Ship Canal Company had plans well advanced, the Farnworth

Journal headline read, 'Improvement of the Irwell,' announcing that 'The Bridgewater Navigation Company will enter at once upon the works for the improvement of the rivers Mersey and Irwell decided upon.' These were reported as being 'deepening and widening of the rivers and the construction of new locks, weirs &c.' The work was to cost £300,000 and was assumed to be an attempt to stave off the proposed Manchester Ship Canal.

The Manchester Ship Canal Bill finally gained royal assent in August 1885, proposing to use, with some modifications, the course of the rivers forming the Mersey & Irwell Navigation. Once the new Ship Canal Company had secured the finance, the assets of the Bridgewater Navigation Company had to be purchased to permit work to proceed. Both waterways were sold to the Canal Company in 1887 for £1,710,000. The single cheque - dated 3rd August - was the largest ever presented at that time.

Edward Leader Williams

The Manchester Ship Canal

The Manchester businessmen who supported the Ship Canal movement did so less because they were dissatisfied with existing transport routes - though the waterway options were inefficient and often expensive - than because they were opposed to the extortionate dues levied by the Port of Liverpool. Such a ship canal venture had first been seriously considered in 1824. The initiative was finally taken by the engineering industrialist Daniel Adamson, who convened meetings of the city's business and civic leaders in June 1882.

The outcome was that two engineers present were to submit a plan for consideration in the September. These men, a Hamilton Fulton, described as a navigation engineer, and Edward Leader Williams, the engineer to the Bridgewater Navigation Company and also the adjacent Weaver Navigation, differed in opinion so much that they submitted separate schemes.

Fulton proposed a tidal canal blasted out to provide 22 feet depth of water through to Manchester. This would have resulted in the Bridgewater canal being 65 feet above the tide level ship canal. To attain the proposed clearance for large ships below, he suggested that a section could be incorporated into the Bridgewater to lift it a little higher (presumably by locks!). The downfall of this scheme was the fact that any terminal docks at Manchester would be about 100 feet below ground level.

Leader Williams offered a locked canal, with the river dredged to near Warrington then canalised with four locks

Daniel Adamson, of the Dukinfield engineering firm, hosted the first meeting of city leaders at his house, The Towers in Didsbury

to Manchester. He proposed high level or swing bridges for road crossings, a tunnel beneath for the railway and a swing aqueduct for the Bridgewater Canal at Barton.

Meeting in September, the group adopted Mr Leader Williams' proposal. A committee was formed to draft a bill to Parliament, for which plans were deposited in the November of 1882. This bill was not proceeded with in that session of Parliament, being dismissed in August 1883.

Undeterred, the promoters submitted a modified scheme to Parliament in December 1883. Among the changes was the proposal to have a channel in the Mersey only as far as tidal locks at Runcorn. Further inland, locks lifted the water level to Manchester. The railway crossing was to be by a high level bridge and again a swing aqueduct was to carry the Bridgewater Canal. This bill was rejected by Parliament in August 1884.

A third attempt at approval brought a further, even more radical, change to the submission that was deposited with Parliament in December 1884. The entrance had been moved downstream to tide locks, a type capable of dealing with the range of tides met with at Eastham. Inland, locks were to be at Latchford, Irlam, Barton and Mode Wheel. Crossings included swing and high level bridges, but still a swing aqueduct at Barton.

This bill was passed by the Lords, subject to the promoters raising £5 million within two years, plus the cost of purchasing the Mersey & Irwell Navigation.

Royal assent was gained in August 1885.

The Swing Bridge and Aqueduct

The death sentence for the two venerable masonry structures crossing the river navigation at Barton-upon-Irwell came with the passing of the Manchester Ship Canal Act. Edward Leader Williams, who had proposed the scheme eventually adopted, was appointed Engineer to the new company. The sale of the interests of the Bridgewater Navigation Company to the Ship Canal Company in 1887 meant that work on converting the line of the old river to a ship canal could go ahead.

Since it was proposed to bring large, sea-going vessels to Manchester, both the Barton road bridge and the Bridgewater Canal aqueduct had to be replaced with structures which would allow the passage of ships. Swing road bridges had been a feature of river (and later, conventional

canal) crossings for at least a hundred years, and it had been intended from the outset to accommodate most road crossings over the canal with a bridge of this kind. Designing large ones, hydraulically operated, would not have daunted the inventive Victorian engineer. Extending the principle to an aqueduct was the novelty.

Fortunately, Edward Leader Williams had already viewed a comparable problem in the Anderton Boat Lift, where watertight caissons moved barges in water between the River Weaver and the higher Trent and Mersey Canal. At Barton, his design for a centrally pivoted swing aqueduct satisfied all the criteria. Discharging the water from the aqueduct trough at every operation had been

An artist's impression of tide locks on the Ship Canal, published in 1888

considered, but there were numerous objections to this. Taking the water from the Bridgewater Canal would cause supply problems, particularly in dry weather. Since the Bridgewater was relatively clean, pumping a replacement volume from the Ship Canal (essentially the heavily polluted water of the River Irwell) was not desirable. Finally, the time required for such an operation went against the idea. The tank had to be swung containing its water.

Both bridge and aqueduct structures were to be founded on a common island in the Ship Canal waterway, which in the Barton section was to have its level raised some sixteen feet above that of the old river. The road bridge was to be erected on the exact site alignment of the old stone bridge and was to be of bow-string girder construction (an arch with a tie across it to resist the horizontal thrust) and the road deck would form the bottom chord of the structure. The original aqueduct was to remain in use until the new one was ready, so the latter was sited some

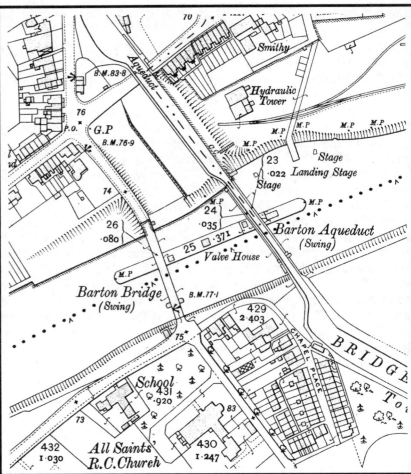

An Ordnance Survey plan from the early twentieth century, showing some of the changes brought by the Ship Canal. The lock and weir of the old navigation have gone and the island for the swing bridge and aqueduct stands in the widened channel. The tower of the hydraulic pumping station is shown between the waterway and the houses on Barton Lane

A PREHISTORIC CANOE.

A discovery of extreme archæological interest has been made upon the Barton section of the Manchester Ship Canal. On Wednesday, whilst the excavators were at work in what is known as the "Salt Eye" cutting, the steam navvy brought to light a prehistoric canoe. It was embedded in the sand about twenty-five feet below the surface. With some difficulty the canoe was removed to a shed in the vicinity of the engineer's office, and examined. It was found to consist of a portion of an oak tree roughly hewn and fashioned.

From the Manchester Guardian of 5th April 1889

twenty-five yards upstream (or east) of the old one. The new aqueduct was to be formed of top and bottom booms, cross-braced, with the tank forming the waterway taking the place of a road deck in an ordinary bridge. Each boom was to be built up of wrought iron plate and angles riveted into position. A contract for both structures was given to Messrs Andrew Handyside of Derby and London.

Heavy excavation works had been carried out at other parts of the route for some time before work began at the bridge site, and in 1889 these works provided some archaeological interest. A prehistoric dugout canoe, together with tree trunks of a similar date, was found in the cutting being made at

Barton in April. In December, workmen found an inscribed stone at the Trafford Hall cutting. The section engineer, Walter Longley Bourke, had it retained, believing it to be the shaft of an eleventh century cross with runic inscriptions.

Preliminary works on Barton's bridges began on the south bank in 1890. One of the first steps was the compulsory purchase and demolition of the Roman Catholic school built at the expense of the landowner, Sir Humphrey de Trafford. It had gone by 1st March, when the Farnworth Journal carried an engraving depicting the scene from upstream and before demolition. Fortunately the school was rebuilt in a location more convenient to the pupils.

With the Ship Canal work under way in May 1889, onlookers line up at Barton Bridge

Works of this magnitude obviously attracted spectators from all ranks of society. The visit of Leopold, King of the Belgians, to the Ship Canal, when His Majesty was escorted by Mr Leader Williams through the Salford, Barton and Irlam sections of the works, was reported in the Farnworth paper on 5th April 1890. With reference to those lower down the social scale, it was anticipated that 'the hundreds of visitors and sightseers who congregate at Barton Bridge on fine Sunday afternoons to view the progress of the works of the Ship Canal will be increased ten fold during the coming Easter holidays.'

The same article explains the need for the Trafford land: 'The principal work here is now being concentrated upon the tunnelling on the south side of the aqueduct, through which, when completed, the river will

October 1892: men at work at the base of the island which supports the swing bridge and aqueduct

be diverted from its present course, so that the foundation for the swing bridge may be put in hand as early as possible.' The river diversion to the south of both stone bridge and aqueduct was certainly necessary for works of the magnitude intended at Barton. Methods previously used, such as caissons to exclude water, could not encompass the area needed or the depth envisaged. The work could only reasonably proceed with the whole area 'in the dry'. A contractor's railway was laid beneath the arches of the existing bridge and aqueduct, whilst the swing bridge's island was to occupy the site of the south piers of the old bridge. At the same time, work was proceeding in preparing the main waterway channel near the old bridges. The public must have been reassured to know that 'While blasting is proceeding a signalman is stationed on Barton bridge. This

A steam crane on the contractor's railway in a sandstone cutting next to Barton Bridge

is very necessary, for only a few days ago a pretty large piece of rock was sent through the roof of a neighbouring cottage.'

The blasting operations were described as 'progressing very favourably' by 31st May 1890, by which time 'the red sandstone rock, which is somewhat thick near to Barton Bridge, has been largely

A pointsman's cabin alongside the railway which passes through arches of bridge and aqueduct on the Stretford side. The fencing above the parapet guides travellers to the temporary wooden bridge, which can be seen on the right of the picture

quarried from the cutting, though much remains to be done. Nearly half of the turnpike bridge, nearest Trafford Park entrance, has been demolished, and a strong temporary wooden structure, from the road to that part of the bridge which spans the river, has been erected.' This temporary bridge is shown quite clearly on a photograph of 12th March 1891. A deviation of the road course has been made on the Trafford bank, with the wooden bridge skewing across to meet the stone bridge at the centre of the pier nearest Trafford. The abutment for the new swing bridge is shown, positioned on the original road alignment.

Operations must have progressed well during the summer, for by 2nd August highly visible construction works are reported: 'The piers and abutments for the swing aqueduct and swing road bridge at Barton have reached a considerable height, and the workmen are busily excavating and levelling the vicinity so that the river may be diverted very shortly. A heading in the rock under the present river is being driven for the gas and water pipes'. Presumably these services had been carried within or on the outside of the old bridge rather than laid in the river bed. (Services carried beneath the present Ship Canal include a sewer in the form of an inverted siphon.) While the papers praised this rapid progress, the sleep-deprived residents of Eccles may not have been so happy, since 'blasting operations in the dead of night [were] continually heard... reminding one of the bombardment of a town.'

Good fortune with the weather was soon to change. Autumn brought rainfall so heavy as to flood completely several sections. The Latchford and Runcorn districts suffered particularly badly, with flooding causing not just stoppage of work but major damage and plant loss. In the closing weeks of 1890 there were delays at Barton, too, as a result of extensive flooding of the works.

The report of the shareholders' meeting printed in the Farnworth Journal of 7th February 1891, whilst generally favourable in tone, does hint at some delay. It notes that 'The work at the ends of this aqueduct is now again in progress. The foundations of the centre pier are nearly all out. All the solid rock and the concrete and brick work will immediately be commenced.'

All must have been well, for with the approach of summer, bridgeworks were clearly being given priority. A report on the progress of the canal works published in the Eccles Journal of 10th April states, 'The concrete pier for the swing aqueduct has already reached a

Work in progress on the Eccles side of the swing aqueduct in February 1891

substantial height; and portions of the ironwork made by Messrs Handyside & Company, of Derby and London, have been delivered.' That night the road traffic at Barton Bridge was diverted over the temporary wooden bridge, which used the road deviation already made, to take traffic in the space between the old stone bridge and the stone aqueduct. Not only did it have to cross the intended Ship Canal channel, but also the temporary river diversion channel and dividing bank, so its span was considerable. The Eccles Journal's sister newspaper, the Farnworth Journal, reported on 18th April that 'The important and conspicuous work at Barton aqueduct and bridge proceeds satisfactorily.'

With the temporary bridge in operation, work could begin on the removal of the old stone bridge and on 9th May the Farnworth Journal reported that it would 'soon be demolished by the Ship Canal workmen. Already a great portion of it has been taken away'; what remained was 'chiefly the old bridge as it originally existed.' Obviously the workmen were removing the newer portion first, including the keystone, for a large block of stone was carefully taken down, on which was an inscription to the effect that road and bridge had been widened and improved in 1830: 'Charles Carrington, bridge surveyer.'

The article goes on to complain that 'The boarding of the wooden temporary bridge has greatly obstructed the view of the works at Barton, and now visitors have to resort to the aqueduct for a sight of them. On Sundays hundreds of spectators crowd it. Although substantial work has been done during the past month, the effect of the progress is not very apparent. The iron bridge crossing Barton-lane is almost ready for lowering into position, and... will replace the existing portion of the aqueduct at that point.' (In fact, the new iron span over Barton Lane is, like the main aqueduct, some 25 yards east of the site of the stone aqueduct it replaced.)

By August 1891 work had progressed to the stage where erection of the steelwork for the aqueduct had begun. A report on the 8th notes that 500 men had been employed on the Eccles section of the canal 'For some time past', but with water let into the Irwell Park cutting, 'the services of 200 navvies have been dispensed with... At Barton, all is life and work in the construction of the new aqueduct. A circular girder has been placed over the rollers, and resting upon this circular

The beginning of the end for Barton's stone bridge in the spring of 1891. The view is from the Stretford side and shows the wooden fencing of the temporary replacement

girder and upon the steel centre are placed three riveted pieces of work, two of them weighing nearly 28 tons each, the third one nearly 35 tons. These were raised from the ground level by means of some strong [sheer]legs and pulley blocks, and they were got up without a hitch. The hydraulic house has been commenced at Barton, for working the swing aqueduct and road bridge'. (This 'hydraulic house' was probably the power house on the Eccles bank which contained the steam-powered pump machinery and accumulator tower. The valve house, or control tower on the centre of the island, was not completed until after working trials of the aqueduct.)

At this stage of the construction, the section engineer to the Manchester Ship Canal Company left their employ, for what can only be described as massive promotion. On 5th September 1891 it was announced that the Bridgewater Trustees had appointed a new Acting Trustee, as successor to the late Hon Algernon Egerton. This was Walter Longley Bourke, who had been engineer to 'several large undertakings', including the Forth Bridge, was a cousin of Earl Mayo and 'no stranger to Worsley', where he now got to live in the Old Hall.

The removal of Mr Bourke did not slow the works, for a fortnight later the newspaper was reporting substantial progress: 'The iron aqueduct which is being erected at Barton... is now assuming a tangible shape. During the past three weeks great progress has been made with it. The walling from it to the new iron bridge over Barton-lane, is all but complete.' A photograph dated 21st September shows a side view of the structure lacking only the uprights at the very outer extremities, the ones to mate with the land abutments. So there had either been a considerable time delay between the writing of the Journal report and its publication on 19th September, or very swift progress of work in two days. The report was correct in saying, 'Workmen are busy with the pivot on which the road bridge will centre and the circular stone groove (sic) is ready for the iron rollers on which the bridge will be supported in revolving. Very few navvies are now to be seen about the Barton section, owing to the advanced state of the works.'

Early in 1892, the Manchester Ship Canal Company radically altered its organisational structure and stopped using direct labour. On 30th January it was announced that the

On the island beneath the swing bridge in July 1892. The photograph shows the hydraulic engines which still power the turning mechanism

Company had decided, with a view to speedy and economic completion, to let as much as possible of the remaining works by contract. In order to secure a free hand, they had given three months' notice at the beginning of the year to many of the engineering staff.

In May, notices were posted at Barton and Eccles, to the effect that the works were closed on Sundays to visitors and passes were not available. Visiting hours on Saturdays were also limited. Whether this was as a result of new management or because the works had reached a critical stage is not clear, but presumably the edict did not apply to the nobility. On 27th August it was reported that Lord and Lady Ellesmere visited the Barton section, accompanied by Mr and Mrs Bourke, of the Old Hall, Worsley. 'They were conveyed on the Bridgewater Canal from Worsley landing stage, in the barge which belonged to the first Earl.'

Whatever the reason for discouraging spectators, there had been noticeable advances by midsummer: 'The completion of the Ship Canal swing aqueduct... proceeds

Barton swing bridge nears completion

slowly but surely. A large number of men are engaged on the road bridge and it is evident that it will be ready for use before the other. The buttress, on the Patricroft side, on which one end will rest is now being prepared... This week, several hundred men have been engaged... and the excavation of earth under the bridges at Barton is now in full swing.' Thus the Farnworth Journal of 18th June kept its readers informed.

The end of the year saw work on the road bridge virtually complete, allowing excavation of the main channel beneath the bridges to proceed. However, the weather intervened. Printed on 16th December, this paragraph tells the story: 'For several weeks past, a large number of navvies have been engaged in blasting and taking out the portion of the embankment at Barton Bridge. Its height has also been considerably reduced,

Crossing Barton swing bridge in the days before traffic congestion became a problem

especially at the end nearest St. Catherine's Schools. The object of course, is to clear away as much stone and soil as possible before letting in the waters of the Irwell which are diverted through a small channel at present; and to diminish the process of blasting under water, which has proved somewhat expensive... The heavy rains of last week and the rapid thaw of snow caused the waters of the Irwell to be swollen... sufficient to flood the works; and the result is that a number of men are temporarily out of employment.' All was not doom and gloom, though, as 'on Tuesday, [13th December] the heaviest swing bridge in the country was successfully turned into position at Trafford Road on the Ship Canal.'

At the end of January 1893 conditions had improved and 'Ship Canal operations just now at Barton are more active than they have been for some time past.' The channel on the All Saints side of the pier had been widened and deepened, and as the temporary wooden bridge was in the way of the excavation work, it was decided

to pull it down and open the swing bridge, in its fixed position, to traffic. Other obstructions and incomplete hydraulic machinery would have prevented full operation, even for test purposes. The opening should have taken place on 1st January, but frost set in, and 'the entrances to the bridge from Barton and Patricroft have only been paved with stone during the past few days.'

It was only a short delay. On 28th January, a large type headline proclaimed 'BARTON SWING BRIDGE OPENED', the article giving a good account of the disappointingly low key affair. The new structure was described as 'a handsome iron swing bridge, weighing 800 tons [actually 640 tons], and 135 feet in length... built by Messrs. Handysides and Company, and will be worked by hydraulic machinery... Its deck is paved with wooden sets fixed in concrete, and is provided with a parapet on each side of short timbers.' Once again, the Journal made an error in its report - the bridge is about 200 feet long and no wooden

parapet was ever provided. Photographs of building operations clearly show a waist-high iron trellis to safeguard pedestrians on both outer edges of the bridge. Short timbers were used to make the actual narrow footways, and this may have been the source of the confusion.

Mr Radford, the County Bridgemaster, had intimated that he would inspect the bridge on Friday 27th January and pass it for traffic purposes. News soon spread and at the hour fixed there were several hundred people waiting at the approaches, kept in order by the local constables. None of the Ship Canal directors was present, as the opening was an informal one. The first vehicle to cross was a cab containing the Bridgemaster, the Mayor of Eccles (Alderman J C Mather) and Deputy Mayor Samuel Mellor, who drove across the bridge from All Saints amid cheering. No speeches were made. Other cabs followed and people flocked on to the bridge from both sides. A Patricroft carter drove a cart of brushes and tinware to and fro and a

Barton road bridge in the late 1960s

cyclist also passed over the new bridge.

Meanwhile work on the swing aqueduct was progressing satisfactorily and by the time the road bridge was opened, the iron gates of the aqueduct bridge were ready and fixed in position. A crucial stage was reached in the last week of April when it was decided to admit water to the tank for the first time.

A favourable report on 20th May read, 'During the early part of the week, a quantity of water was pumped into the new iron swing aqueduct at Barton for the purpose of testing its condition. At the end facing Patricroft there is a slight leakage, but otherwise it fully answers expectations. The water will be run out and the defective part remedied.' It seems likely that this exercise included some trial of the hydraulic machinery, as on 3rd

June it was noted that a 'recent test was eminently successful'.

Opening the new aqueduct to traffic must have been seen as a possibility, for the May article continues, 'A large number of men are engaged removing the embankment at each end dividing the new waterway from the Bridgewater Canal.' There were difficulties, however, in proceeding with the earthworks for the Ship Canal channel. Following heavy rain, a barrier gave way at midnight on Wednesday 17th May; as a result, 'for the third time the water has invaded the workings at Barton Bridge. It will take fully a week to pump it out again, and in the meantime about 120 navvies will be thrown out of work.'

It was these civil engineering works forming the approach channel to the aqueduct which caused serious problems when first filled with water. The

Farnworth Journal of 3rd June 1893 described what happened on Monday 29th May, when it was decided to let in water to the new section: 'The approaches at each end were blocked off [from the old canal] by pile work... About two o'clock, in the presence of Mr Parker, the engineer, and his assistants, and other Ship Canal officials, one of the piles was cut off below the level of the water, and amidst the cheering of a large number of spectators the water flowed swiftly into the new diversion, which is some 375 yards long.' (The total length is 200 yards on the Barton side, 75 yards of aqueduct and 100 yards on the Stretford side.)

'By five o'clock the water had reached the full height, and everything appeared to have gone on satisfactorily. A few minutes afterwards, however, it was discovered that a serious leakage was taking place some

The pump which was used to fill the aqueduct when the tank was tested in May 1893

15 yards from the iron [aqueduct]. Water rushed out in a large volume from under the heavy boundary stone wall on the Eccles side, and the low lying land was quickly flooded. A hut belonging to the men was carried a short distance away, and the gardens at the back of the cottages in Barton-lane also became inundated. Another volume of water ran on the opposite side of the diversion and found its way into the Ship Canal.'

As soon as possible the flow of water from the Bridgewater canal was stopped and the gates of the iron bridge shut. As the isolated section became dry, the damage was visible. At the spot where the leakage occurred, the bed of the canal had completely subsided and 'The force of the water had created a large hole, leaving the brick archway quite visible. The soil underneath the arch, principally of a sandy nature,

Preparing to let water into the new approach channel on 29th May 1893

Working on the new section of the canal between the bridge over Barton Lane and the swing aqueduct. Two years after this photograph was taken, the back gardens of the houses on the right were flooded when the canal bed subsided

was all washed away, and it is believed that a portion of the arch itself has collapsed. Parallel to the fissure and running a distance of several yards the concreting has become detached from the side of the wall and the puddling thereabouts washed away.' The engineer, Mr Leader Williams, was informed and pending an enquiry, all visitors were prohibited and Barton Lane closed.

By the middle of August, the deviation had been repaired. Its bed, re-laid with concrete and puddle, was being gradually filled with water, but this time caution prevailed: 'It will be thoroughly tested before being used for traffic.' For over a week it was tested, at full depth of water, and no leakage was found. The officials of the Ship Canal decided to open it on Monday 21st, so over the weekend, two crane boats were employed in pulling up the piles at the Trafford Park end.

Then they proceeded through the new portion to the Patricroft end, where on the Monday morning the piles were taken out and a small dredger removed the remaining soil.

There was even less fuss over the opening of the new aqueduct than over the swing road bridge. The newspaper account of the great day, Monday 21st August 1893, betrays at least one journalist's disappointment: 'Shortly after noon preparations were begun to connect the old hauling path with the new one by temporary bridges across each end of the old aqueduct. Whilst this was proceeding, the ordinary traffic was allowed to pass through the new waterway. The first boat entered from the Stretford end at a quarter past two. It was the "Ann", of Lymm, laden with carboys of vitriol. It was boarded by a number of spectators, who thus had the pleasure of the first ride through the swing caisson...

The "Helen", laden with coal from the Bridgewater Collieries, passed through to Manchester... Thus the new waterway was opened without any ceremony whatever. Some 500 people assembled on the old aqueduct and waited a considerable time in the expectation of Lord Ellesmere coming in the Queen's barge... and formally opening the new portion... there had been no such intention.'

As soon as the new deviation and aqueduct were completed, demolition operations began on the old one. By the first weekend of September progress was rapid, for 'This week the number of workmen engaged in pulling down Brindley's Aqueduct over the Ship Canal at Barton has been greatly increased, and the work pushed on night and day.' Such was the quality of the stonework that explosives had to be resorted to, but fortunately it appears that the Industrial Preservation Movement was born at Barton.

Looking along the old line of the canal, across the bridge over Barton Lane, towards the Dutton Arms on Barton Road

The portion spanning Barton Lane was attacked on 30th August and cleared by 2nd September. The face and buttresses of this arch were covered with masons' marks and 'The worthy Councillors whilst negotiating hit upon the happy idea of preserving that side of the archway and its two buttresses which face Barton Post Office.' Mr Wills, the contractor, readily agreed to give them the stonework 'so that the inhabitants might have the arch re-erected as a monument of Brindley's historic "castle in the air".' The newspaper report quite rightly concludes with the sentiment, 'The Borough of Eccles is to be heartily congratulated.'

Barton memorial arch, photographed in 1894. The stonework was preserved by rebuilding the structure alongside Barton Lane

The finale of the aqueduct construction came on Friday, 13th October 1893. The following day readers were told, 'a very interesting operation took place at Barton, when the new caisson and road bridges - the destruction of the famous Brindley aqueduct being completed - were turned round for the first time.' This left only the completion of the channel for the Ship Canal, until the papers of Saturday 4th November had to report 'Another Mishap at Barton.'

On the previous Saturday, the Barton Lane farmer had noticed water leaking from the new deviation of the Bridgewater Canal, 'close to the iron bridge which spans Barton-lane. A small stream was running

Men working on the puddle of the new section of canal near the swing aqueduct in 1893. On the left can be seen the elevated towpath approach

down the enamelled brickwork into the roadway.' The prepared stop planks were placed in the canal by the cranes set for the purpose and the aqueduct gates shut, and as soon as the water was run off a fissure was visible in the puddle bed along the stone wall. It was thought that this was how the water had found its way through the concrete and under the wall. Over Saturday and Sunday a large number of men were put on and by Monday had cleared the clay puddle and concrete. New concrete was put in and the puddle replaced by Wednesday.

The aqueduct in motion. The closed end of the Bridgewater Canal on the Stretford side can be seen on the right

Water had also been coming out on the earth embankment against the stone side wall and this was cleared for quite a distance. The newspaper report continued, 'it would seem, from the fact that stout wooden supports have been fixed against the wall, that the stone work had either settled a little or given way, thus causing the leakage. At any rate workmen are busily enagaged in building stone buttresses against the sidewall to support it, and the

rest of the embankment of earth is being put back in a more solid fashion than before.' The Bridgewater Canal was not expected to open until Sunday 5th November at the earliest, but since there was a major coal strike on at the time, the traffic on the canal was minimal.

All must have been well for the official opening of the Manchester Ship Canal on 1st January 1894. Once again a momentous occasion passed, as

the local papers said, 'without undue ceremony, with a formal opening to take place later, perhaps at Whitsun. The Canal directors led the way from Runcorn, aboard the first ship.'

With the construction project complete, the tidying up of the works depot sites became a priority. One left-over which, given the working methods of the period, must have had quite a lot of use was the Ship Canal Accident Hospital on Peel Green Road, near the swing bridge. This had, in fact, been sold some time earlier to the Barton Local Authority, but they had second thoughts and put it up for auction. The sale notice of 3rd February 1894 describes it as an 'excellent built WOODEN ERECTION, comprising tongued and grooved Boards, Flooring Boards, panel Doors and Casings, sash Windows and Frames'. There was also a kitchen range, parlour and other grates, cooking stoves, baths, a lavatory and wash bowls, a hot water boiler and water and gas fittings. Included in the sale were a new ambulance carriage and the left-over 'quantity of Drugs'. The whole 'has been built and fitted up regardless of cost, and is in splendid condition'. Nevertheless, if nobody wanted

The Ship Canal Accident Hospital, photographed in September 1889

the whole thing, the Authority was prepared to sell it piecemeal.

Apart from delays caused by bad weather, the road bridge does not seem to have suffered from any constructional or structural problems during the course of its erection. This soon changed. Difficulties were experienced in turning it during the September after the Canal opened, and lasted for about a week. In one instance it took over an hour to move the bridge to its full extent. An examination showed that one of the 64 steel rollers on which it turned had broken into pieces. This meant that the road had to be closed overnight, from 10pm on Friday 20th September 1895, so that new rollers could be fitted.

Technical details of the swing bridges, their specification, construction details and mode of operation are given in several contemporary publications. One of the best general descriptions appears in the local newspapers of June 1893, which

also recount the abortive attempt to open the aqueduct to traffic. Presumably the details had been given out as an unfortunately premature press release.

The media published it anyway, rightly acknowledging what had been achieved: 'The new aqueduct is a masterpiece of engineering skill. It represents by far the most formidable task the engineers have had to meet in the construction of the Ship Canal, and is a unique piece of mechanism. Briefly, it consists of a long tank turning on a pivot fixed on a pier in the centre of the Ship Canal. When in its normal position it is continuous with the line of the Bridgewater Canal.' The working of the gates which shut off the water at each end of the tank, together with a separate pair of gates keeping back the water in the land channels, is described as an 'ingenious piece of machinery, precise and delicate almost as that of a watch... The aqueduct may then be bodily swung round, lengthwise, with its contained

tons of water, to allow passage of ships along the greater waterway beneath.' Although the total weight of the aqueduct when laden with water is 1,450 tons, of which the water in the trough weighs some 800 tons, 'the mere pulling of a lever effects the change of position.'

The same article goes on to describe the swing road bridge, but with some inaccuracy: 'A little higher up the Ship Canal than the pivot aqueduct is a swing bridge, weighing 600 tons... The structure is of iron, and is constructed on the cantilever principle, as the angle at which it crosses the canal would not permit of an exact centre balance. The arms are respectively about 90ft. and 60ft. in length.'

In fact the swing road bridge crosses the Ship Canal at right angles; the arms are of differing lengths because the island is offset to permit the two widths of Ship Canal waterway, 90 feet on the south side and 60 feet on the north. It is easy to see how the figures got misinterpreted.

The 'Manchester Producer' being towed past Barton Aqueduct

The southern arm actually measures about 112 feet, comprising seven bays at 13 feet 9 inches and one at the land edge of 16 feet. The north arm is some 82 feet long and consists of six of the 13 foot 9 inch bays.

Each end of the road bridge is curved to the appropriate radius and the mechanism is so constructed that the bridge may be swung in either direction, but obviously not all the way round. Other additions to the hydraulic machinery on the road bridge include a locking bolt, to secure it to the abutment. There is also a jack at each abutment corner; these operate only when the bridge is open to road traffic, to stop oscillations building up were the bridge to sway. When it was built, the deck, of iron plates, had a road surface of timber setts, laid on concrete with the end grain upwards and jointed in bitumen.

Conversely, the aqueduct does cross the Ship Canal at an appreciable angle, a feature that assists its operating principle. The moving tank is symmetrical about its pivot centre, with the ends bevelled so that immediate clearance is created on opening. Thus, movement is only possible one way; the ends to the abutments turn anti-clockwise on opening for traffic on the Ship Canal. The difference in Ship Canal waterway widths is compensated for by having the north abutment set back from the Ship Canal bank.

The complexity of the hydraulics and the dimensions of the aqueduct were discussed in the technical press, notably in the January 1894 issue of 'Engineering', which gave full details. The box girder construction was 22 feet wide and 33 feet deep at the centre, tapering to 28 feet 10 inches at the ends. The main girders were 234 feet 6 inches long, and the tank 19 feet wide, with a water depth of 6 feet. A timber fender ran along the water line and the towpath was 9 feet above water level. The article described how four massive columns are based on the turning gear with the two booms cantilevered out from these. The sides of the tank are of single thickness plate stiffened with angle irons, whilst the underside consists of a double skin plus four girder beams. Each side of the aqueduct consists of five bays with the girders arranged in the criss-cross pattern known as warren girder design (after the mid-nineteenth century engineer James Warren).

Just as important to the working of the swing aqueduct are the civil engineering works and mechanism on land. On the south bank, a short span brick arch and pillar reach out into the main waterway, carrying a wrought iron tank section large enough to accommodate the landward stop gate. The north bank has abutments of sandstone masonry forming an embankment, reinforced with wrought iron through ties and cast iron 'spreaders', possibly put in after the construction mishaps. This is surmounted by brick walling forming the water channel sides and housing the land stop gate. Superimposed on this wall, arches in blue brick supported the towpath approach ramp. Both abutments carry the sealing wedge described later.

Between the main aqueduct and Barton Lane is the embankment of masonry, brick and earth that caused so much trouble in the final stages of construction. Barton Lane is crossed by a wrought iron trough of single plate, reinforced with angles on the outer sides and with eleven shallow beams below, all riveted together.

The railed towpath above the water level can be seen in this drawing of the aqueduct published in 1897

Hydraulic power came from a

pumping station on the Eccles bank of the Ship Canal, near the aqueduct. This brick building with its tall chimney contained two sets of equipment, one operational, the other on standby, supplied by Messrs Galloway of Manchester. Steam from Lancashire boilers fed horizontal, compound, non-condensing engines (that is, with two cylinders for high and low pressure, with the exhaust steam vented to the atmosphere). These drove pumps of the three throw ram type, three cylinders in line with the ram forming a piston, each working in sequence to provide water at 650 pounds per square inch. The power plant site also had an hydraulic accumulator tower where water under pressure was stored, this tower being comparable in size to the valve tower sited on the bridge and aqueduct island.

When both structures are open and their ends are over the island, they are separated by this four-storey valve house, which once also contained an engineer's store and workshop. The turning movement is

A tug photographed upstream of the aqueduct. The tower and chimney in the background belong to the hydraulic pumping station

controlled from the valve house and originally water was pumped from the Eccles bank to valves below island level. The valve rods rise through the middle two floors to the lofty, glass-sided control room, with its commanding view along the major waterway.

The hydraulic engines which turn the bridge and the

An 1892 view showing the solid island structure on which the bridge and aqueduct turn

aqueduct are also below island level and have timber cabin covers, which can be seen to the east of each crossing. The original engines were of the three-throw oscillating type in which power was maintained by having three cylinders with pistons working in sequence. They were made by Sir W G Armstrong Mitchell Ltd of Newcastle and again there were duplicate sets for each structure, one in use, the other on standby. Each set has its own drive via reduction gearing - a bevel gear and vertical pinion shaft - to the turning ring gear. A manually-operated dog clutch between engine and gearing isolates the turning engine which is not being used.

The turning mechanism beneath both structures is much the same. A cast iron race plate (25 feet mean diameter for the road bridge, 27 feet for the aqueduct) is solidly bedded to the granite blocks of the island. On this run 64 cast iron rollers, 14" diameter at the outside, tapering to 12" over their 32" length. All these are kept in position by a spider ring. An upper cast iron race plate

The control tower on the island

supports the massive base ring of the structure and in turn, the deck (or in the case of the aqueduct, the tank). The drive is transmitted via the aforementioned pinion shaft to a circular gear rack above the upper race plate.

Both the bridge and the aqueduct were built with the central pivot in the form of an hydraulic jack. Known as the 'centre press', its purpose was

to relieve pressure on the rollers during turning. In the case of the aqueduct, the ram was 4'9" diameter and exerted an 800-ton upward pressure.

For the aqueduct to work, it was essential to keep the water in the tank at all stages. Technically the most difficult part of the cycle is when it is positioned in line with the Bridgewater Canal. Beginning with the tank aligned to allow barges to pass along the Bridgewater, this is how it operates:

First, the four gates - two sealing the ends of the tank and two the landward abutments - are closed. These are recessed into the channel side, and pivoted at one edge to swing out, sealing their respective waterways. They are moved by a hydraulic engine which drives a pinion shaft against a quadrant on the gate pivot. Each gate also has a hand crank mechanism as a back-up, all these being housed in four cabins at the gate positions. Since there is a space between the gates on the tank and those on the abutments when closed, this has to be drained - or filled - by valves operated from the gate cabin.

An engineer admires the steel rollers on which the aqueduct turns

Even with the advantage of the bevelled end to the tank, some clearance between tank and abutment is required to allow for seasonal expansion. To make up this space and provide a waterproof seal, the most ingenious mechanism on the aqueduct is employed. Each land abutment has a steel wedge, faced with indiarubber and made into a much elongated U shape to correspond to the profile of the sides and base of the tank. On closure the 12-ton weight of the wedge is enough to maintain a watertight seal between tank and land. When the bridge is opened, each wedge is lifted by two hydraulic rams outside the line of the tank. Their extended piston rods guide the wedge, together with two additional

Handyside's works plate, still visible on the bridge

guides below the wedge and within the line of the tank, to give sufficient clearance for the tank to be swung.

The bolt which locks the tank in its closed position, in line with the Bridgewater Canal, is released by hydraulic operation from the gate cabins before the engines driving the turning mechanism are started. These hydraulic engines have their force transmitted through reduction gearing before setting in motion the pinion turning the structure.

Both bridge and aqueduct were constructed in the same way, of what all contemporary reports refer to as 'wrought iron'. Modern investigation has revealed the material to be mild steel comparable to BS grade 43a. It was supplied as plate or section in transportable pieces from Messrs Handyside's works. A works depot was set up adjacent to the construction site and the equipment to cut, shear, punch and drill was installed. Most of this machinery was readily portable, hydraulic-powered and intended for use outdoors, as was the normal procedure in

Crossing Barton Aqueduct in the late 1960s

shipyards and bridgeworks. It meant that pieces could be assembled or adapted on site to suit exact measurements. In whatever manner the pieces were produced they had to be hoisted into position for the final riveting work. Whilst steam cranes were certainly used, the normal means of placing portions of ironwork on to the structure would be by block and tackle suspended from timber sheerlegs.

The process of riveting was very labour intensive and demanded a well organised team. First the pieces to be joined, often three or more plies of metal, were placed together and the holes aligned by forcing taper drifts into some of them. Then a rivet, heated in a coke- or oil-fired hearth by a boy, was taken out and tossed to the riveters. It was caught with tongs, still glowing and put through the hole so the existing dome head was against the work. The rivet could then be 'closed' by the other end being formed into a dome, so that when the rivet cooled, the pieces were gripped tight. Rivets on the bridges were

mainly threequarters of an inch in diameter and a good team could 'close' about 800 in a day.

In workshop conditions, or in fairly accessible places in situ, all rivets were closed using a hydraulic rivet press, portable enough to be swung by crane to each rivet. This method gave a more certain integrity of rivet than did manual hammering. On the bridge itself, the rivet heating fires, and the gangs to close them, were stationed at whatever height the joint happened to be. Some indication of the work involved can be gained from the count of rivets; in only one vertical leg of the aqueduct, there are about 700 visible.

The hydraulic services machinery and pipework had to be put in at the appropriate time and thus co-ordinated with the civil engineering, masonry and structural work. Mains for hydraulic power had to be laid from the power house on the Eccles bank to the control tower on the island, and within the masonry of the abutments to operate the landside equipment to the

gates, jacks and lock bolts. This was accomplished by providing a service culvert beneath the bed of the Ship Canal to take the cast iron pipes conveying pressure water.

Apart from the early incidents, any operational and maintenance difficulties have been the result of fair wear and tear. Considering the weight of the swing bridges and the frequency with which they are turned, it would be surprising if there had been no problems at all. The potentially embarrassing scenario of the bridges being rammed by shipping was avoided by swinging them well in advance of the ship arriving, so that in the event of malfunction, the ship could be stopped.

The only recurring event to affect the travelling public has been the frequent expansion of the road bridge in summer, when it has either refused to open, or once opened, refused to close. The remedy has proved to be an exercise for Eccles Fire Brigade, who douse the structure with undiluted Ship Canal water.

Eccles Fire Brigade hose down the road bridge in the summer of 1982

After thirty years of intensive working, swinging many times in a 24-hour day, it became apparent that the supporting roller unit of the aqueduct was suffering. The cast iron roller path plates had worn by an inch and the rate of wear was accelerating. In July and August of 1927 the roller race was completely replaced, with Sir William Arrol & Company as contractors. Cast steel was substituted for the original cast iron for both upper and lower race plates and the rollers, and the granite bed had to be re-cut so that thicker plates could be used. In 1938 a similar operation was carried out when the rollers were replaced on the road bridge. One change made in each case was that use of the hydraulic centre press was permanently discontinued, without adverse effect on the operation of either bridge or aqueduct.

A year later, in 1939, the turning engines on the aqueduct were replaced by a pair of radial, three-cylinder engines manufactured by the Hydraulic Engineering Company of Chester and soon after the start of World War Two, in 1940, a change of power source was made. Twin, electrically driven pumps were

The electric hydraulic pressure pumps in the new power house on the island

installed in a new power house situated on the island, to the west of the aqueduct. The suppliers, Mather & Platt of Manchester, provided a pair of electric drive suction pumps to lift Ship Canal water to header tanks on the island. Water is taken from these tanks by a pair of electric drive axial pumps to provide the hydraulic pressure of 600 pounds per square inch. As with the earlier machinery, the duplication allows one of each to be on standby. The old steam power station was demolished after the war.

A press report of a hydraulic

mechanism failure in November 1958 did have a touch of farce about it. The bridges had been swung and the ship passed through. It was then realised the hydraulics had failed, leaving both bridge and aqueduct closed to traffic. For some reason all the bridge crew were on the central island and there was no telephone. It was some hours before they succeeded in summoning help as, fortunately for most bridge users, the incident took place on a Sunday morning. Only the crew and churchgoers were inconvenienced.

Visually, the most striking change was some time in the 1980s, when the aqueduct was painted in red and white instead of the grey micaceous oxide retained on the road bridge. Less noticeable is that the aqueduct no longer carries a towpath. To save width, this once necessary feature had been placed at a high level, some nine feet above the water level of the Bridgewater Canal and was cantilevered from the western arch of the swing aqueduct. It was approached by a lengthy ramp from the Eccles bank, of which only the supporting brick piers remain. On the Trafford side the steep, sett-paved ramp now makes an excellent viewing platform.

The original hydraulic engines installed in 1892, still turning the road bridge in 2002

Barton High Level Bridge

The swing road bridge proved good enough for the horsedrawn traffic of Edwardian Trafford Park and Eccles. But in the years between the World Wars the use of motor transport increased, and with this came longer and longer delays for both goods and passengers. It became obvious the swing bridge was inadequate and in 1925 the Manchester & District Joint Planning Committee reported a proposition for a new road to relieve the congestion at Barton. Throughout the Second World War there was serious disruption to the transport of war workers and materials to the vital industrial plants of the Park and this led to the first post-war suggestions of an alternative crossing.

Immediately after the war, and even more when the period of strict austerity began to ease, the problem became acute. Often, hundreds of workers at a factory could be late for their shift. Multiply this by the many major employers, and the scale of the difficulty is apparent; it was felt on both sides of industry. Employers lost production and employees lost pay, as being 'bridged' was not accepted as an excuse for lateness. The Manchester Regional Plan of 1945 incorporated a Stretford and Eccles by-pass and by 1949 the Road Plan of the Lancashire County Council indicated that the by-pass part should be of motorway standard.

Some relief came when the Ship Canal Company made the concession of only swinging the bridge during off-peak hours, but this obviously inconvenienced the ship owners, as boats could miss tides. As the number of vehicles continued to increase, the bridge itself became a bottleneck, enforcing single line traffic in each direction. Further problems were caused by its weight restriction and local agitation culminated in a meeting in April 1951, when Eccles Town Council took up the fight. They had called a conference of other local Councils affected, local and County highway officials, trades unions, employers' federations and shipping interests.

The first practical work on the project began early in 1953, when the County Council allowed the tipping of industrial waste from the Lancashire Steel Company's works at Irlam. This material was placed so as to form the basis of the approach embankments. By 1955, optimistic noises about a relief scheme were being made by the County Council, culminating in a statement in April to the effect that a start on a high level bridge could be expected within three years. Official wheels moved more quickly than expected, as during the February of 1957, there was a Government Inquiry into the County scheme for a seven-mile by-pass between Stretford and Worsley, to include a high level bridge. If the order, valued at over six million pounds, was confirmed, work would start immediately.

In this case, 'immediately' was not a figure of speech, for on Wednesday, 10th April 1957, thirty years of campaigning for a new Ship Canal Bridge reached the final stage. On that day the Chairman of the Lancashire County Council inaugurated the work, when he opened a valve to start a steam hammer to drive the first pile for the foundations of the bridge. The Eccles Journal of 5th April carried a preview artist's impression, the first public view of the construction plan for the Stretford - Eccles motorway.

The by-pass was to be a dual carriageway 5.95 miles long, with a high level bridge crossing the Ship Canal

A traffic problem on Barton Bridge in the 1950s

threequarters of a mile west of the swing bridge. The new bridge was to be one of the longest motorway bridges in the country. It would reach 97 feet above water level with a length over the bridge and viaducts of nearly half a mile. Its deck was to be 73 feet wide, with twin 24-foot carriageways, a 9-foot central verge and 6-foot side verges. The main bridge over the Ship Canal would be a three-span structure consisting of a 310-foot central span and two 175-foot side spans. On the south bank a viaduct would be formed of four spans at 115 feet and one at 135 feet, with the north viaduct being nine spans at 115 feet and one at 135 feet.

The main girders were to be of welded steel, to carry a reinforced concrete deck on reinforced concrete piers built on piles which would be driven or bored according to the condition of the ground. The whole would require 5,000 tons of structural steel, 2,000 tons

reinforcing steel and 20,000 cubic yards of concrete. George Dew & Company of Oldham were appointed main contractors.

Translating the contractor's tender into reality hit a snag. By July it was apparent that steel of the grade required was in short supply; the national economy was booming and there were overwhelming demands for steel by the shipbuilding industry. The Eccles Journal of 26th July reported both problem and solution. Although ten firms had tendered for the bridge, only one of them - the most expensive - could get the special steel for certain parts of the welded design. Even that firm could not guarantee to get it within the period required. Discussions with George Dew & Company and their sub-contractor for steelwork indicated that 'They are prepared to construct the bridge with an all-riveted

superstructure at an additional cost of £68,188 above their tender figure.' The County Council recommended they accept this lowest tender of some £1,746,000. Work proceeded on this basis, with Samuel Butler Ltd appointed as steelwork sub-contractor.

Whilst the steelwork was being got ready, preparatory site works proceeded and a New Year report in January 1958 declared that all was running to schedule. The culverting of Salteye Brook was 70% complete and the work of piling for the pier foundations of the high level bridge was well under way. Pictures of progress on the Stretford side were published throughout the year and show scaffolding and formwork (the framework to hold the fluid concrete) for the piers together with the building of the earth embankment. Material for the long approach embankment came from many sources, but chiefly from the Hollins Green dredging tips; the Lancashire Steel Corporation works at Irlam also contributed further vast quantities of infill material.

Throughout the summer of 1958 the Eccles paper carried progress reports and photographs. The issue of 11th April showed the piers that would support the bridge on the Urmston side; the earthwork embankments were approaching the furthest landward one, which was at the stage of having concrete poured into the formwork of its crosshead (the part which joins the two piers across the top). The piers nearer the water still consisted only of the pier legs, or simply of scaffolding. By 1st August, another photograph of the Urmston side showed considerable progress. All six concrete piers were complete and the four landward spans of steel girders were in position. A further photo published on 5th September gives a close-up and end-on view of the eight girders

Summer 1958: progress on the high level bridge as seen from the Urmston side

forming the span, equally spaced in two groups of four.

Soon after this, progress on the major steelwork was such that they were preparing to erect the long span which would overhang the Ship Canal waterway. 10th October brought the announcement that Samuel Butler Ltd, the steel contractor, would be undertaking a 'big job' on the bridge, in lifting sixteen girders on to the piers, each one 265 feet long and weighing 116 tons.

Butler's had bought what was then one of the largest cranes in the country specially for this operation. It was of the stiff-legged derrick type, with a jib of 131 feet, capable of lifting 40 tons. In the task of lifting the 116-ton girders it was supplemented by another piece of lifting equipment, an A-frame or sheerlegs, capable of lifting 90 tons. The 16 girders, eight on each bank, would form the two anchor-cantilever spans of the bridge. They were among the largest ever used in bridge construction in this country and it was estimated that it would take two to three hours to swing each one into position.

A photograph published on 12th December shows the crane in action. Then, as now, Germany had the monopoly in

Concrete piers for the high level bridge in 1958

supplying high capacity cranes to the construction industry and the machine had had to be brought from Hamburg. Unfortunately this caused adverse comment in the Eccles Council chamber and was also the subject of a question to the Minister of Transport, when he visited Urmston.

Early in the new year of 1959 there were reports of construction problems, when 'Some difficulties had been caused by soft silt beneath the approach embankments'. However, remedial work was undertaken and it was 'not anticipated that the completion date would be affected.' The concreting of the viaduct was 'proceeding well'.

Disaster struck at 4.15pm on Thursday, 19th February 1959, when tubular trestling collapsed on the Urmston side of the Ship Canal and three men were killed and four injured, one of whom died on the Sunday following the accident. The trestling was supporting four 105-ton steel girders, of which two had already been fixed. Then the four 50-ton sections of the remaining two girders were hauled into position, ready for riveting. They were 80 feet above the ground and 30 yards from the Ship Canal bank. Men were working both on the girders and beneath them when a crane driver saw the trestle begin to crumple. As he shouted a warning, all the girders and trestling collapsed, trapping men beneath and the crane driver in his cab. Acetylene burners were used to cut a way through the wreckage to reach the dead and injured.

Later the following week a statement was issued by George Dew & Company, the main contractors, following what they described as many sensational and distorted press reports. It said, 'The fabrication and placing of the steel girder[s] was sub-let to an old established firm of specialist constructional steelwork engineers... This firm, in turn, sub-contracted the design and

Girders being raised on to the piers in the winter of 1958/9

erection of the temporary tubular steel supporting trestles to one of the principal steel scaffolding firms in the country.' Six of the seven men involved were employed by the constructional steel company and one by the scaffolders.

The statement continued, 'The use of trestles to support steel girders in position until such time as they are completely assembled and self-supporting on the permanent piers is the normal practice in bridge construction where the girders are too heavy to be lifted in one piece... The cause of the collapse of the steel trestles has not been determined but is being investigated by all parties.' Apart from superficial damage to the concrete of one pier, 'The accident has caused no damage whatever to any part of the work permanently completed.'

It further noted that work had not halted, but the wreckage had been left in position whilst investigations were carried out. The delay to the high level bridge was likely to be two months, not the twelve months suggested. The cost of work caused by the accident would be borne by the contractor.

The report of the inquest on the bridge disaster victims published on 20th March disclosed working practices now scarcely comprehensible. It was found that the trestles had not been constructed to the design drawing, that the tubular steel was corroded and that no qualified engineer had passed the design. Expert witness Professor W Merchant of the Manchester College of Science and Technology said, 'the trestles were not adequately designed or properly manufactured. All parties concerned in the design and construction of the bridge failed to realise that the two trestle towers which collapsed were important structures which merited proper engineering design and supervision.' The drawing provided was 'only an indication of the structure and not a working drawing. It omitted many items such as the size of tubes, and the numbers of joints and bracing tubes.' The tubes supplied were much used and corroded; some of the joints had gaps between the tube ends and thus were not load bearing.

The tower designer, a twenty-four-year-old draughtsman at the scaffolding company, had no formal qualifications. Details of the job he had got from the site were simply that the scaffold was to support four 105-ton girders, a total of 420 tons when they were complete. He considered that each tower would carry half the total weight and that if each tower was constructed to carry 240 tons, they would be adequate. He submitted designs of both three- and two-tower format respectively, based simply on the load-bearing capacity of the support tubes. Messrs Butler, the steel contractor, chose to accept the two-tower design.

In reply to Butler's the professor said that the two-tower format was suitable, providing everything was done correctly. Mills & Company, the scaffold contractors, did not accept all that the professor had said. A verdict of accidental death was recorded, the coroner making the plea that future such operations should be given the proper engineering supervision.

By the end of March the crashed girders had been scrapped and new ones made at Scunthorpe, and it was anticipated that steel erection would continue in the next few weeks. According to a progress statement, 'After the anchor arm and cantilever spans on the Urmston side have been completed, those on the Peel Green side will be placed into position and then the actual bridging of the Manchester Ship Canal by a suspension span will be tackled.' A photograph published in mid-October shows both approach spans

A photograph taken a few hours after the accident in February 1959

complete and the north side beginning to cantilever out over the Canal.

Unfortunately, labour relations between the steel erectors, then known as spidermen, and the steelwork contractor, Samuel Butler Ltd, had reached such a low point with repeated disputes and strikes that Dew, the main contractor, terminated Butler's contract. Work stopped on 18th December. This stoppage, and the disruption preceding it, laid the basis for yet another disaster.

The contract for finishing the erection of the steelwork was let to the United Steel Erection Company, who put some men to work on Wednesday 30th December. Labour relations were still tense, as the new workers rejected a plea by the ninety spidermen recently dismissed, not to start work.

The men found a site in chaos, with stores of bolts missing or misplaced, small items of steelwork wrongly fixed or even stored on the wrong canal bank, and worse, few drawings available.

Once they got up to the high level steelwork, they found that only the main girders numbered 5 to 8 had been permanently erected by Butler's. Girders 1 to 4 had been raised but only rested on the concrete pillars, and were misplaced by up to four inches in level and alignment, with the vital bracings missing, or secured with only one bolt instead of the intended four. It was later determined that only 10% of the vital cross bracing was in place when they began work on aligning and securing these girders to the anchor cantilever span on the Eccles side of the canal.

Lacking a supervising engineer, the foreman decided to begin operations by correcting the position of girders 1 to 4, on the Eccles side of the bridge. It is likely that the new men felt they had to make a show of doing something, so after only a few hours on site, they began to jack the four 256-feet long girders into their correct position. While they were attempting this, girder 4 toppled sideways, followed, domino-like, by girders 3 and 2, and then girder 1 fell - part of it the 75 feet to the ground - bringing down the tubular scaffold, which simply crumpled. A roll call established that two men were dead and eight injured.

Once again, local emergency services were faced with a serious incident. Perhaps most involved were the police, who had to maintain traffic flow, control crowds and preserve evidence. Their conduct gained the coroner's commendation.

Also affected was the Manchester Ship Canal. All shipping had to come to a standstill and another major incident was narrowly averted when a 4,000 ton vessel was pulled up only fifty yards short of the wreckage which the crashing girder brought down into the canal. Divers were employed to clear a safe passageway for shipping. A further inconvenience was the fallen girder and wreckage lying across the Manchester Ship Canal Company's railway.

The inquest began with a two-day hearing, where again Professor Merchant gave his opinion on the shortcomings of the operation. At the inquest, the foreman responsible for the incident told of the hostility from other employees felt by his men. The degree to which relations between the outgoing contractors and United Steel had been soured was apparent in the opening remark of United Steel's QC to Butler's

A photograph taken the day after the accident of December 1959, showing an inspection party on the collapsed girders